No. 1183
$12.95

TROUBLESHOOTING MICROPROCESSORS & DIGITAL LOGIC

BY ROBERT L. GOODMAN

TAB BOOKS Inc.

BLUE RIDGE SUMMIT, PA. 17214

FIRST EDITION

SECOND PRINTING

Copyright © 1981 by TAB BOOKS, Inc.

Printed in the United States of America

Library of Congress Cataloging in Publication Data

Goodman, Robert L.
   Troubleshooting microprocessors and digital logic.

   Includes index.
1.   Digital   electronics.   2.   Microprocessors—Maintenance and repair.   3.   Logic circuits—Maintenance and repair.   4.   Microcomputers—Maintenance and repair.   I. Title.
TK7868.D5G66   621.3815   79-25162
ISBN 0-8306-9950-3
ISBN 0-8306-1183-5 pbk.

Cover photo courtesy of INTEL Corp.

Preface

There is no doubt about it—a whole new ball-game is in progress for the electronics service technician as he moves into logic- and microprocessor-equipped devices that are now rapidly coming onto the consumer market. These items run the gamvt from digital clock timers to sophisticated video game terminals and microprocessor-controlled home microcomputers.

This book will contain practical digital/logic troubleshooting information for the electronics hobbyist. You may wish to think of this as a "service workshop in a book" about digital device servicing where we will have a meeting of the minds on these very sophisticated marvels. In fact, some of the applications the microprocessor can now perform will just about "blow your mind." Plus, almost every day some new device or technique crops up.

Two things which come to mind and are boggling at this writing are the bubble magnetic memory chip and research on ways to actually manipulate the atoms within a solid-state device to read and write back millions of memory data bytes that are nonvolatile.

This book explains basic digital logic information and microprocessor operation, plus ways to troubleshoot them. Care has been taken in writing this book so that the TV and electronics technician can understand these concepts and then put them into practical use.

The main purpose of this book is to help you dig right into the digital logic operating systems and quickly locate and solve any problems. Not only will dual-trace triggered-sweep scopes and logic probe be used for these troubleshooting methods, but your *own* logic will be brought into play.

This book begins with a basic introduction to digital techniques and applications. We will look at various logic gates, hardware and software. Next will be a peek at microprocessor design, programming techniques and computer language information.

Ways to use the scope for testing, (TTL) logic gates and clock pulses will be given next, along with how to capture glitches, or spikes, on a scope or logic probe. Then regulated DC power supply checks will be covered. More logic probe testing techniques follow that. How to use a probe pulser generator to jog a pulse through various gates for frame freeze time IC testing.

Then a description of various microprocessor chips found in current consumer products and ways to service them in actual bench check operations. These chips found in color TV and stereo systems will be thoroughly covered.

The book continues by delving into operation and troubleshooting of direct address remote control color TV systems with electronic tuning. This section will also include some notes on phase-locked loop (PLL) operation and testing techniques.

Moving onto another section, some selected logic circuits and ways to troubleshoot them, as pertains to video tape recorders (VCRs) and videodisc players, will next be encountered. Home and hobby microprocessor-based minicomputers systems will be next on the agenda, and we will look at some actual operations and system diagnosis.

The next item to be dealt with is video TV games. This will include game operation, service tips and how to troubleshoot video TV games.

Robert L. Goodman

Contents

Acknowledgements

I am very grateful to the contributions of the following companies and personnel:

Texas Instruments Inc.—Bob Fuller

Lab Science for the photos and information on their versatile VLA-1000 logic analyzer

Heuristics, Speechlab for minicomputer systems

Zenith Radio Corp.—James F. White

General Electric Co.—J.M. Surprise

Continental Specialties Corp.—Barbara Bachman

Magnavox Corp.—Ray S. Guichard

Sony Corporation of America—Howard L. Katz

GTE/Consumer Electronics—E.M. Nanni

B&K Dynascan Corp.—Myron E. Bond

INTEL Corporation—Mike Peak

Hewlett-Packard Corp.—E.A. White

The Tandy Corp. Radio Shack—Dave Gunzel

RCA/Consumer Electronics—J.E. Scallions

A special thanks to Mr. Frank W. Gregorio, director of publications for E&L Instruments, Inc., for granting me permission to use information from their series of BUGBOOKS. And of course, many thanks to the authors of the BUGBOOK series:

Peter R. Rony
David G. Larson
Jonathan A. Titus

Chapter 1
An Introduction to
Digital Logic Techniques

Electronics and microcomputers in particular, could not be what we know them today, if the integrated circuit was not developed. There is no doubt, that the space age spawned the IC chip.

DETAILED IC INFORMATION

An IC is an electronic device, usually constructed from semiconductor materials, in which transistors, diodes and resistors are manufactured simultaneously to make a tiny functional electronic circuit. The IC wafer that contains the transistors, diodes and resistors may be no larger than 30 mils on a side.

For a better perspective of the integrated circuit, we need to look at the trends in the electronics industry over the past 30 years. All electronic gear 30 years ago was built with discrete components. These components were fabricated before being installed in the equipment and included resistors, inductors, capacitors and vacuum tubes. The gear was very bulky and heavy. It also consumed lots of power. With vacuum tube computer installations, one had to contend with a frequent occurrence of burned out tubes and large rooms full of equipment—also, a huge electric bill.

The transistor became a direct competitor of the vacuum tube, with almost a complete take-over of equipment by 1970. At first, transistors were discrete components that were fabricated prior to their installation in electronic equipment. As semiconductor technology improved, the transistors were able to tolerate higher and operate up to higher frequencies. The higher frequency characteristic became important in the second generation of computers, which used discrete solid-state components.

The basic concepts for integrated circuits were developed during the late 1950s. By 1965, semiconductor manufacturing technology had improved so much that semiconductor firms were able to fabricate circuits on individual silicon wafers that contained many transistors. Such circuits were no longer discrete circuits. Transistors, resistors and diodes were manufactured simultaneously 500 to 1000 at a time. These large wafers are then scribed into smaller chips that are then individually mounted into a plastic or ceramic package. The IC package is then plugged into sockets or soldered onto a printed circuit board or plug-in module.

In the late 1960s the chip makers went from the small scale integration to medium and then large scale chip integration. Small scale integration refers to integrated circuits that provide only simple gates, buffers and flip-flops. Such chips usually contain no more than 10 to 20 gates. In medium scale integration, the IC chips function as simple, self-contained logic systems such as counters, small random access memories, decoders, multiplexers and shift registers. Such chips usually contain from 20 to 100 gates. Large scale integration refers to integrated circuit chips with a complexity of greater than 100 gates or gate-equivalent circuits. Currently, many microprocessor chips contain the equivalent of several thousand gates on a single piece of silicon wafer that measures 170 mils on a side.

Probably all will agree that remarkable changes have occurred in the manufacture of semiconductor electronic devices. The cost of manufacturing a transistor within an integrated circuit has dropped to less than 0.04 cents per transistor in 1979. The technology associated with each integrated circuit transistor has also been improving. Today's gates, which are manufactured from transistors, have decreased power requirements and increased speed. The lower the power requirement per gate, the more gates that can be placed on a small silicon wafer because of less heat to dissipate. Today's microprocessors have almost surpassed the best large computers of the mid-1950s.

INTERNAL CHIP CIRCUIT DIAGRAMS
In order to troubleshoot digital IC circuits effectively you must know how the internal gate connections are wired to the chips pin-out leads. You will also need a diagram or symbol drawing in

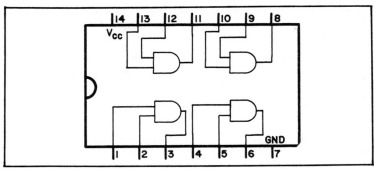

Fig. 1-1. Internal connections for the 7408 IC.

order to design or wire-up an integrated circuit chip. As an example, we will now look at ways to represent the internal wiring of a 7408 quad 2-input positive AND gate chip. The drawing layout pin configuration is shown in the (Fig. 1-1) drawing.

The number 7408 is assigned to all quad 2-input positive AND gate chips that have this pin configuration and the electrical specifications of the original 7408 chip, which was developed and manufactured by Texas Instruments in the late 1960s. This type of chip is available from five or more different manufacturers, including National Semiconductor, Sprague, Signetics, Stewart Warner and, of course, TI. The term *quad* indicates that these are four separate 2-input positive AND gates on each 7408 chip.

The *positive* notation refers to the fact that the gates function as AND gates when positive logic is used. Of course, negative logic may also be used with chips designed for this purpose. Finally, you will note that each gate contains two inputs; hence the 2-input designation.

Any of the 7400-series of integrated circuit chips have only two power inputs—ground (GND) and supply voltage (Vcc) input pin. The letters V5CC represents +5 volts, although the chip should function if Vcc is anywhere in the range of +4.75 volts to +5.25 volts. If the input supply voltage goes above +6 volts, it is very likely the chip will burn out in a short time. If the power connections are reversed, and you apply +5 volts to the GND pin, and ground the Vcc input pin, they will also be burned out. Perhaps you can save the chip if you act quickly under these conditions. Remember, though, that a burned out chip (shorted) will usually be quite hot to the touch.

The pin configuration for the 7400 quad 2-input positive NAND gate chip is very similar in appearance to the 7408 IC chip, as shown

13

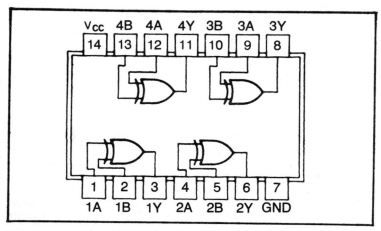

Fig. 1-2. Connections for the 7400 2-input NAND gate IC.

in Fig. 1-2. Like the 7408 chip, the power inputs are at pin 7 and pin 14. The chip contains four independent 2-input NAND gates that can be represented as in the Fig. 1-3. Always keep in mind that none of the gates can function if power is not applied to the V_{cc} pin.

The drawing layout for the 7486 quad exclusive-OR gate chip is shown in Fig. 1-4. This 7486 quad contains four independent exclusive-OR gates that are represented in Fig. 1-5.

DIGITAL SIGNALS AND PULSES

Digital signals are discrete or pulse signals whose various states are discrete intervals apart. The typical digital signal (Fig. 1-6) in digital electronics is a binary signal, which is defined as a voltage or current that carries information in the form of changes between two different states that are a discrete interval apart. One of these states is called the logic 0 state, and the other is called the

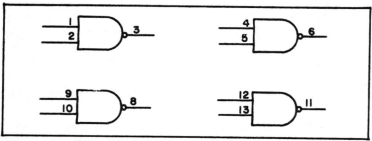

Fig. 1-3. The 7408 has four independent NAND gates.

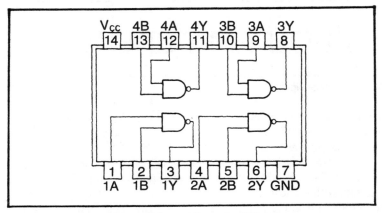

Fig. 1-4. Internal layout for 7486 quad Exclusive-OR gate.

logic 1 state. For voltage signals, the logic 0 state is typically at ground potential, whereas the logic 1 state varies between +3 and +5 volts. For current signals, the logic 0 state is typically the absence of current 0 mA and the logic 1 state is generally set at 20 mA.

To help you visualize these logic off-on or high-low states, refer to the square-wave pulse train shown in Fig. 1-7. These states may also be referred to as zeros and ones. A gate input, to be valid, must be positive (high) or grounded (low).

Thus, a key point to remember is that any gate can have only one of two possible states for its input or output logic mode. To identify these two possibilities, one state is called one and the other zero.

Almost all modern digital logic circuits are now TTL, which is the shorthand for transistor-transistor logic. Thus, the input devices for the gates are transistors and not diodes or resistors.

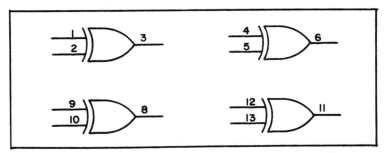

Fig. 1-5. Four independent Exclusive-OR gates are found in the 7486 chip.

15

Fig. 1-6. Typical digital signal pulses.

These gates are referred to as DTL and RTL. Digital circuits at the block diagram level are much simpler than the analog circuits that most hobbyists are used to working with. The TTLs are two-state devices with precisely defined logic levels. The pulse drawing shown in Fig. 1-8 indicates the high and low states for TTL. When working with static logic levels, the voltmeter or scope can be used to detect high and low states. The pulse drawing indicates the 0 to 0.8 volt DC is considered to be low, while 2.4 to 5 volts DC is a high state for TTL circuitry.

The region in between is known as the *undetermined* state. In logic systems troubleshooting, an undefined state would usually indicate some type of circuit fault.

Each high and low pulse has a positive-going and a negative-going edge. The TTL gate circuits then detect these transistions, and it is these edges that are used as the actuating signal. Only the positive-going or negative-going edge is required to make the next logic device go into operation.

RESISTOR-TRANSISTOR LOGIC

We will now take a brief look at the resistor-transistor logic (RTL) family of devices. The best advantage of the RTL logic is its low cost, but it has a very slow speed. RTL logic could not be

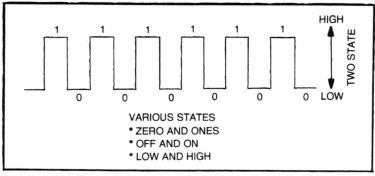

Fig. 1-7. Digital logic 0 and 1 pulse states.

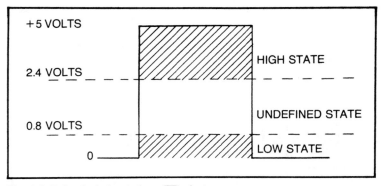

Fig. 1-8. Pulse logic levels for a TTL device.

utilized in the high-speed microcomputers of today. The RTL logic device consumes considerable power, has a limited drive capability and is quite noisy in operation. Its operating speeds will generally be less than 10 million counts per second.

NOR GATES

Basic RTL operation can be realized with resistors and transistors alone as a NOR function. An RTL NOR gate is shown in Fig. 1-9.

The RTL NOR gate operates in this way. When both inputs A and B are low, the base-emitter junction is reverse biased and the transistor is cutoff. Thus, there is no current through R, so Q

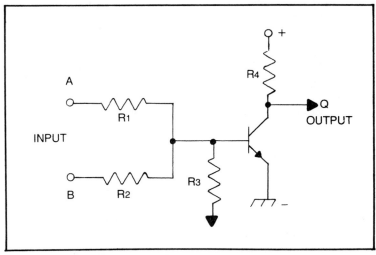

Fig. 1-9. An RTL NOR gate circuit drawing.

17

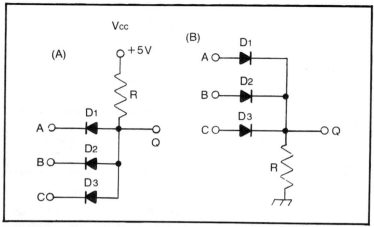

Fig. 1-10. Diode-resistor logic AND gate (A) and DRL OR gate (B).

remains high. However, if one or both of the inputs are high, the base-emitter junction is forward biased; the transistor is conducting and Q now goes to a low state. The gate circuit now functions as a NOR gate.

DIODE GATES

Before we look at diode gates, let's review briefly basic diode and transistor characteristics. A diode is conducting when forward biased (when the anode is positive with respect to the cathode) and cut off when reverse biased. A transistor is conducting when the emitter-base junction is forward biased and the collector base junction is reverse biased.

The basic circuits for the AND and OR resistor diode logic gates is shown in Fig. 1-10. First, let's look at how the diode logic gate works, shown in Fig. 1-10A. In this circuit, logic 1 corresponds to +5 volt (high), and logic 0 to 0 volts (low).

If all the inputs A, B and C are low, all three diodes will be conducting so that output Q will be low. In terms of positive logic, this means that when A, B and C are 0, Q is also 0. And when only one or two of the inputs are low, Q is still at low.

Only when A, B and C inputs are high will all diodes be cut off so that no current can flow through R, with the result that Q is high too. When all inputs are logic 1, the output is also logic 1. This is the correct definition for an AND function.

When we use negative logic, this circuit becomes an OR gate. If all inputs are high (logic 0), all diodes are cut off and Q remains high. Should one or more inputs be low, the diodes in question will conduct, current will flow through R, and Q will become low (logic 1), which is the function of an OR gate.

Now let's check out the operation of the OR gate circuit shown in Fig. 1-10B with positive logic. When all inputs are low (logic 0), no current flows through R, so Q remains at ground potential (low = logic 0). However, when one or more inputs go high (+5 volts = logic 1) the diodes in question conduct, current then flows through R, and Q becomes HIGH. A DTL NAND gate is shown in Fig. 1-11.

TRANSISTOR-TRANSISTOR LOGIC

The transistor-transistor logic (TTL) family is now the most popular type of gate. Because of its high speed, it is used in all microprocessor systems. The difference between TTL and DTL logic is that instead of an input circuit made of diodes, a transistor is used. Each emitter-base diode serves as an input diode.

The basic function of the TTL gate, as with the DTL gate, is the NAND function. Refer to the totem-pole TTL logic gate circuit shown in Fig. 1-12 as we follow through this operation. If one or more inputs are at ground level (logic 0), current will flow through input resistor R1. This causes the collector of the input transistor to go low. Only when all inputs are high will the collector be high too.

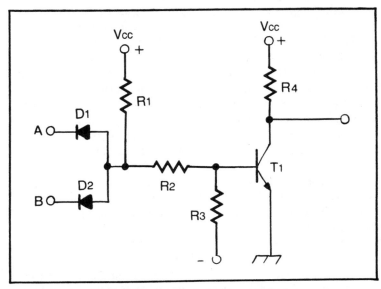

Fig. 1-11. A NAND diode-transistor logic (DTL) gate circuit.

The input circuit actually gives normal AND operation. The next stage acts as a type of phase splitter for driving the totem-pole output. When T2 is cut off, T4 will be on and T3 will be off, resulting in a low output, which is the NAND function. The diode in the output chain ensures that T3 is cut off when T4 goes on.

A disadvantage of the totem-pole output is that no outputs can be connected in parallel (WIRED-AND connections). If two or more TTL outputs were connected together and one output was low and the other was high, this would cause a short-circuit, and power dissipation would be much too high. However, TTL gates with special output circuits (called open collector outputs) have been designed to make WIRED-AND connections possible.

Transistor-transistor logic is commonly referred to as TTL, but may also be called T^2L or "tee squared ell". TTL devices are low cost per gate (and going even lower). They have high-speed capabilities (20 MHz to 100 MHz is typical), good noise immunity, a moderate drive requirement. Also, hundreds of TTL devices are now available. For these reasons, most of the logic devices and troubleshooting information in this book will deal with TTL device systems.

DIGITAL DEVICES

The dictionary definition for a digital device states that it is any system that represents data notations with exact precision. Let's see if we can bring that down to terms we can both understand.

Basically, a digital device can be defined as any device that operates on or manipulates binary. Binary refers to an operation that has two states. You may recall from previous studies that binary coding can be represented by any type of two-state device, such as an on or off light, an open or closed computer card, a north or south magnetized magnetic core or portion of a magnetic tape or disk; two different voltage levels; two different current levels; or two different frequencies. And probably the most familiar symbols are 0 (low) and 1 (high).

In digital electronics, you will find devices that manipulate binary information in the form of voltage levels: +5 volts for the logic 1 state and near ground potential for the logic 0 state. With the state-of-the-art in digital electronics, a change in logic state can be accomplished in less than 2 nanoseconds. Plus the cost of digital devices are still in a nose dive. Thus, speed and low cost have caused digital devices to completely take over in the field of electronics. Some of the digital devices you will encounter in this book

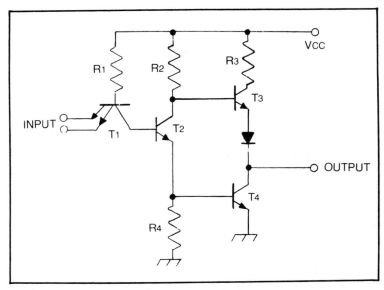

Fig- 1-12. TTL with totem-pole output gate circuit.

are gates, counters, decoders, flip-flops, buffers, shift-registers, multiplexers, memories, encoders, latches and arithmetic/logic units.

The Logic Gate

Probably the most simple digital device is the logic gate. A gate is a circuit that has two or more inputs and one output. Therefore, digital information appearing at the output depends on the combination of digital information that appears at the inputs. Actually, the term gate has various meanings in the electronics field, but in this book we will only consider the digital gate device.

The four common gates are the AND, OR, NAND and NOR gates. A gate that is more complicated can be developed from NOR or NAND gates and is called the Exclusive-OR gate. However, before we dig into gates, the truth table concept will be discussed.

Truth Table Concepts

A truth table chart shows the relationship of all output logic levels of a digital circuit to all possible combinations of input logic levels in a way that shows all circuit functions completely. By input or output logic levels, we mean logic 0 and logic 1 states, which in many digital devices contain voltage levels of 0 volts and +5 volts,

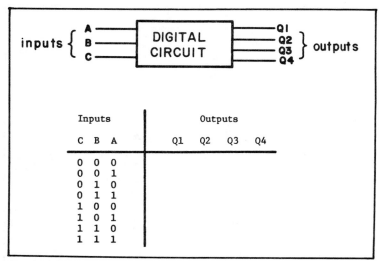

Fig. 1-13. Logic circuit with partial truth table.

respectively. The truth table definition chart may also be rephrased as follows: A truth table shows the relationship of all output logic 0 and logic 1 states of a digital circuit to all possible combinations of input logic 0 and logic 1 states so as to characterize all circuit functions completely.

Figure 1-13 shows a digital circuit that has three inputs (A, B and C) and four outputs (Q1, Q2, Q3 and Q4). The object of the truth table, then, is to give the relationships between the inputs and outputs of a logic device. This is easy since the inputs and outputs can only be zeros or ones. Since there are two possible states per each input, and there are three different inputs, this makes a total of eight different sets of inputs, which are also listed in Fig. 1-13.

On the left-hand side of the truth table you will see eight different sets of three inputs. The logic states of the four outputs will depend upon which digital gate circuits are used. You therefore, cannot complete a truth table for a given set of inputs until you know the specific circuit gates that are involved, or until the name of the specific logic device is given.

Truth tables are used because they are a simple and convenient shorthand representations of digital circuits. It is much easier to devise a truth table than to explain how a specific digital circuit operates. The more inputs and outputs that exist, the more obvious the advantage a truth table is over a written description. Truth tables are used to represent digital circuits just as electrical engineers use circuit diagrams and architects use blueprints for buildings. Truth tables actually show the behavior of digital circuits and represent many words of explanation.

Gates and Their Use

The digital gate functions can be used in many different ways. However, no matter how a gate is used, the truth table for the gate will always apply. A truth table is a basic characteristic of a gate. Thus, it is not altered no matter how a gate is used.

A gating circuit is one in which a gate is used to control the passage of a digital signal, which may be a single pulse, a group of pulses, or a train of pulses.

A logic circuit is an electronic circuit that provides an input-output relationship corresponding to a Boolean algebra logic function.

A memory is any device that can store logic 0 and logic 1 states in such a manner that a single bit or group of bits can be accessed and retrieved. Memory elements can be constructed from groups of gates that are referred to as *flip-flops*.

OR Gate Operation. You will find the symbol and truth table for the OR gate in Fig. 1-14. For the OR gate, the unique state occurs when both input A and input B are at logic 0. This observation is important whenever you want to remember the truth table for an OR gate. Thus, the unique output state, logic 0, occurs when all inputs to an OR gate are at logic 0.

NOR Gate Operation. A NOR gate is a binary circuit with two or more inputs and a single output, in which the output is logic 1 only when all inputs are logic 0, and the output is logic 0 if any one of the inputs is logic 1. The symbol and truth table for the 2-input OR gate is shown in Fig. 1-15.

At this time, we need to note the small circle (on the point of the cone) in the OR gate symbol. This small circle has been shown previously in the NAND gate symbol. In other words, for the NOR

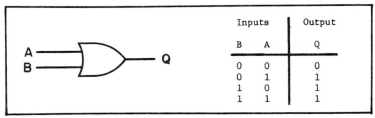

Inputs		Output
B	A	Q
0	0	0
0	1	1
1	0	1
1	1	1

Fig. 1-14. OR gate symbol and truth table.

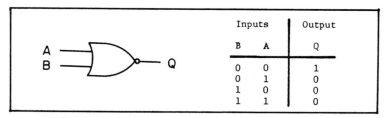

	Inputs		Output
	B	A	Q
	0	0	1
	0	1	0
	1	0	0
	1	1	0

Fig. 1-15. The 2-input OR gate and truth table.

gate, you can treat the inputs as those to an OR gate, and then invert the output. A 2-input NOR gate can be created from a 2-input OR gate and a single inverter, as shown in the Fig. 1-16. Or a 2-input OR gate can be developed from a 2-input NOR gate plus an external inverter. Please keep in mind that inversion, or complementation, can be represented either by the inverter symbol or by the small circle placed before or after a gate or other type of digital device symbol.

The Exclusive-OR Gate. The Exclusive-OR gate can be easily defined by looking at its symbol and truth table in Fig. 1-17. This type gate is closely related to the OR gate, and is sometimes called an Inclusive-OR gate by computer programmers. The only difference between the two occurs when both input A and B are at logic 1. For the OR gate, the output is logic 1, whereas for the Exclusive-OR gate, the output is logic 0. When multiple-input OR gates are used occasionally, the Exclusive-OR gate is typically a 2-input gate.

Exclusive-OR gates are common and can be purchased as integrated circuit chips that contain four such gates on a single chip. Alternatively, a single Exclusive-OR gate can be built from three 2-input NAND gates and a pair of inverters, as shown in Fig. 1-18. If you remember the truth table for the NAND gate and inverter, you can readily demonstrate that this circuit produces the truth table for an Exclusive-OR gate.

AND-or-INVERT Gate. The AND-or-INVERT gate is a composite gate circuit that is used in microcomputer systems. This is not a basic gate. It actually consists of AND gates and a single

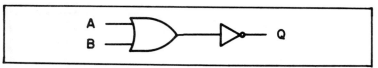

Fig. 1-16. A 2-input NOR gate created from a 2-input OR gate and an inverter.

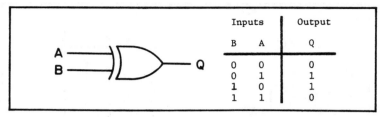

	Inputs		Output
	B	A	Q
	0	0	0
	0	1	1
	1	0	1
	1	1	0

Fig. 1-17. Exclusive-OR gate with its truth table.

NOR gate. Such gates are available with two per integrated circuit chip. When you use an AND-or-INVERT gate, you must specify how many AND gates are included and how many inputs each AND gate possesses. For a 3-wide 2-input AND-or-INVERT gate, this indicates that there exists three AND gates, each of which has two inputs. The symbol and truth table for a 2-wide 2-input AND-or-INVERT gate are shown in Fig. 1-19.

Buffer/Driver Device. A buffer gate or driver is a digital device that increases the power or current handling capability of a binary circuit that is connected to the buffer gate or driver. It is a binary circuit with one input and one output in which the output is logic 0 when the input is logic 0, and the output is logic 1 when the input is logic 1. This should not be called a buffer gate, as there is only a single input. Refer to Fig. 1-20 for the symbol and truth table for a noninverting buffer/driver device.

The output voltage from a buffer or driver is usually +5 volts or at ground potential. Some devices could have more than +5 volts on them. In these cases, the buffer/driver circuits cannot be connected directly to the inputs of other IC chips without damage.

Some Complex Gating Circuits. Many varied and complex digital electronic devices can now be readily obtained from many IC electronic manufacturers. Some of these devices are available at

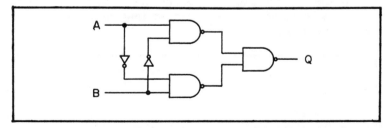

Fig. 1-18. An Exclusive-OR gate made from three 2-input NAND gates and a pair of inverters.

25

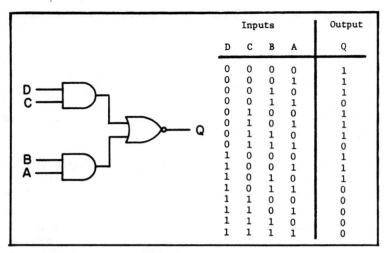

Inputs				Output
D	C	B	A	Q
0	0	0	0	1
0	0	0	1	1
0	0	1	0	1
0	0	1	1	0
0	1	0	0	1
0	1	0	1	1
0	1	1	0	1
0	1	1	1	0
1	0	0	0	1
1	0	0	1	1
1	0	1	0	1
1	0	1	1	0
1	1	0	0	0
1	1	0	1	0
1	1	1	0	0
1	1	1	1	0

Fig. 1-19. A 2-wide 2-input AND-OR-INVERT GATE.

low cost and are IC chips that contain many complex gating circuits, such as decoders, full adders, multiplexers, arithmetic logic units/ function generators and priority encoders.

One example of a complex gating circuit is the truth table and gating circuits for the TI 7442 BCD-to-decimal decoder chip shown in Fig. 1-21. To construct such a circuit, 10 4-input NAND gates, 4 inverters and 4 inverter/buffers are required. This is all fabricated on a single integrated circuit chip. An example of an even more complex gating integrated circuit is the 74181 arithmetic logic unit/ function generator shown in Fig. 1-22, courtesy of Texas Instruments Incorporated. If you study this IC carefully, you will observe AND-or-INVERT gates, Exclusive-OR-gates, inverters, 4-input NAND gates, and 4-input AND gate. This entire circuit is available on a single integrated circuit chip.

In some ways the more complex digital electronics that go into a chip, the easier it is to troubleshoot these systems. The more circuitry *within* a chip, the less external wiring and components you will have to replace or check out.

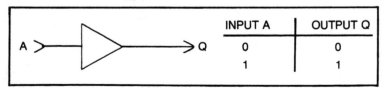

INPUT A	OUTPUT Q
0	0
1	1

Fig. 1-20. Noninverting driver and truth table.

Standard Gate Symbols. The most common standard gate symbols will now be discussed and illustrated. In order to make logic troubleshooting easier, you should try to commit these basic gate symbols to memory.

The following gate symbol drawings will be found in Fig. 1-23: 2-input AND gate, 3-input AND gate, 2-input NAND gate, 3-input NAND gate, 2-input OR gate and 2-input NOR gate.

A more complicated gate, such as the Exclusive-OR gate, which can be constructed from 2-input NAND or NOR gates, is

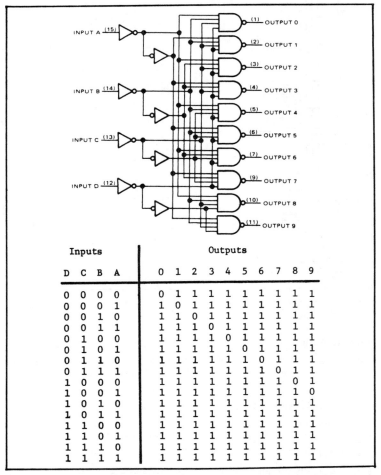

Inputs				Outputs									
D	C	B	A	0	1	2	3	4	5	6	7	8	9
0	0	0	0	0	1	1	1	1	1	1	1	1	1
0	0	0	1	1	0	1	1	1	1	1	1	1	1
0	0	1	0	1	1	0	1	1	1	1	1	1	1
0	0	1	1	1	1	1	0	1	1	1	1	1	1
0	1	0	0	1	1	1	1	0	1	1	1	1	1
0	1	0	1	1	1	1	1	1	0	1	1	1	1
0	1	1	0	1	1	1	1	1	1	0	1	1	1
0	1	1	1	1	1	1	1	1	1	1	0	1	1
1	0	0	0	1	1	1	1	1	1	1	1	0	1
1	0	0	1	1	1	1	1	1	1	1	1	1	0
1	0	1	0	1	1	1	1	1	1	1	1	1	1
1	0	1	1	1	1	1	1	1	1	1	1	1	1
1	1	0	0	1	1	1	1	1	1	1	1	1	1
1	1	0	1	1	1	1	1	1	1	1	1	1	1
1	1	1	0	1	1	1	1	1	1	1	1	1	1
1	1	1	1	1	1	1	1	1	1	1	1	1	1

Fig. 1-21. A TI 7442 BCD-to-decimal decoder chip and truth table (courtesy of Texas Instruments).

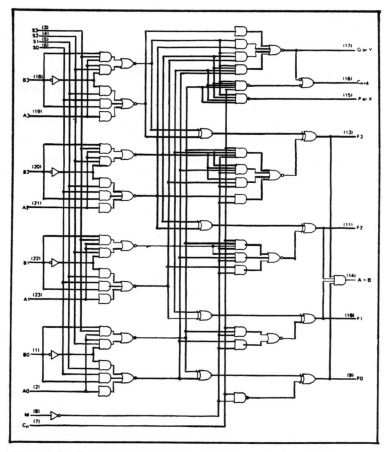

Fig. 1-22. The TI 74181 arithmetic logic unit/function generator chip (courtesy of Texas Instruments).

shown in Fig. 1-24. The symbol for an inverter, which is a single-input single-output digital device, is shown in Fig. 1-25. The symbol for a buffer, sometimes referred to as a driver, is shown in Fig. 1-26.

AND Gate Operation. The behavior or operation of a 2-input AND gate can be stated as follows: If input A is logic 1 and input B is logic 1, then output Q is logic 1. With any other input combination, output Q is logic 0. To help you with the truth table for an AND gate, remember the unique output state: Logic 1 occurs when all inputs to an AND gate are at logic 1. Figure 1-27 shows the AND gate and its accompanying truth table.

28

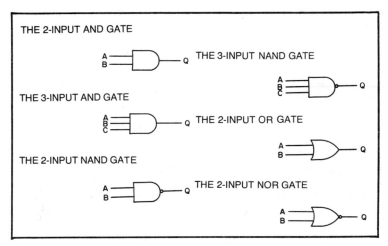

Fig. 1-23. Various gate symbols for reference.

3-Input AND Gate. The operation of a 3-input AND gate is stated as follows: If input A, input B and input C are all at logic 1, then output Q is also logic 1. For all other input logic combinations, output Q is at logic 0. The symbol for the 3-input AND gate and its accompanying truth table are shown in Fig. 1-28. We can now define

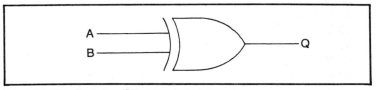

Fig. 1-24. The Exclusive-OR gate symbol.

an AND gate as a binary circuit with two or more inputs and a single output, in which the output is logic 1 only when all inputs are logic 1, and the output is logic 0 if any of the inputs is a logic 0.

NAND Gate Operation. A NAND gate can be defined as a binary circuit with two or more inputs and a single output, in which

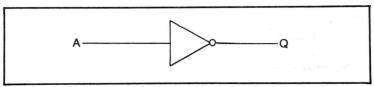

Fig. 1-25. Inverter symbol.

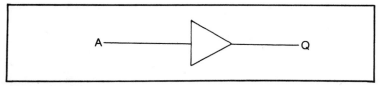

Fig. 1-26. Buffer or driver symbol.

the output is logic 0 only when all inputs are logic 1, and the output is logic 1 if any one of the inputs is logic 0.

The NAND gate is closely related to the AND gate. The one difference is that the output of the NAND gate is the complement of

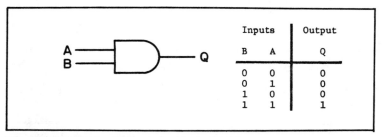

	Inputs		Output
	B	A	Q
	0	0	0
	0	1	0
	1	0	0
	1	1	1

Fig. 1-27. Symbol for AND gate and its truth table.

the output of a related AND gate. The symbol and truth table for the 2-input NAND gate are shown in Fig. 1-29.

If you compare the NAND gate with the AND gate, they will be the same except for the outputs. A logic 1 for an AND gate is a logic 0 for a NAND gate and a logic 0 for an AND gate is a logic 1 for a NAND gate. Logic 1 and logic 0 are said to be complements of each other. Logic 1 is the complement of logic 0, and logic 0 is the

		Inputs		Output
	C	B	A	Q
	0	0	0	0
	0	0	1	0
	0	1	0	0
	0	1	1	0
	1	0	0	0
	1	0	1	0
	1	1	0	0
	1	1	1	1

Fig. 1-28. A 3-input AND gate and truth table.

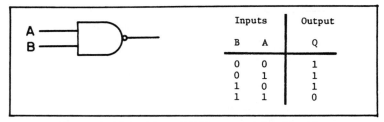

	Inputs		Output
	B	A	Q
	0	0	1
	0	1	1
	1	0	1
	1	1	0

Fig. 1-29. The symbol for a 2-input NAND gate and its truth table.

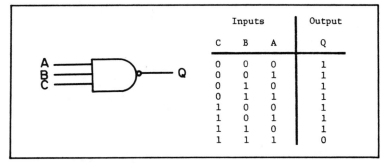

	Inputs			Output
	C	B	A	Q
	0	0	0	1
	0	0	1	1
	0	1	0	1
	0	1	1	1
	1	0	0	1
	1	0	1	1
	1	1	0	1
	1	1	1	0

Fig. 1-30. A 3-input NAND gate with its truth table.

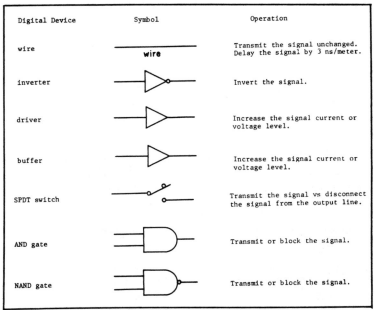

Digital Device	Symbol	Operation
wire	wire	Transmit the signal unchanged. Delay the signal by 3 ns/meter.
inverter		Invert the signal.
driver		Increase the signal current or voltage level.
buffer		Increase the signal current or voltage level.
SPDT switch		Transmit the signal vs disconnect the signal from the output line.
AND gate		Transmit or block the signal.
NAND gate		Transmit or block the signal.

Fig. 1-31. Various electronic devices and the operations they perform on digital signals.

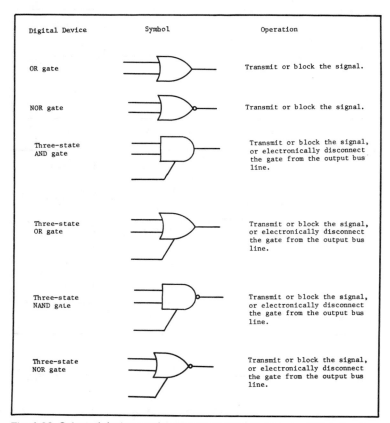

Digital Device	Symbol	Operation
OR gate		Transmit or block the signal.
NOR gate		Transmit or block the signal.
Three-state AND gate		Transmit or block the signal, or electronically disconnect the gate from the output bus line.
Three-state OR gate		Transmit or block the signal, or electronically disconnect the gate from the output bus line.
Three-state NAND gate		Transmit or block the signal, or electronically disconnect the gate from the output bus line.
Three-state NOR gate		Transmit or block the signal, or electronically disconnect the gate from the output bus line.

Fig. 1-32. Selected devices and the functions they perform on digital signals.

complement of logic 1. Figure 1-30 shows the symbol for a 3-input NAND gate and its truth table.

OR Gate Operation. An OR gate is a binary circuit with two or more inputs and a single output, in which the output is logic 0 only when all inputs are logic 0, and the output is logic 1 if any one of the inputs is logic 1. The behavior of a 2-input OR gate can be stated as follows: If input A is logic 1 or input B is logic 1, then output Q is logic 1. If both inputs are logic 0, then Q will be logic 0 also. Included in this statement is the condition when both input A and input B are logic 1, in which case output Q is also logic 1.

The information and device drawings shown in Figs. 1-31 and 1-32 are useful as references when troubleshooting any digital/logic equipment. These reference charts give representative operations that will be performed upon digital signals.

Chapter 2
Microcomputer
Applications and Operations

In this section we will look at some of the terms and definitions for digital computers, data processors, microcomputers and the microprocessor. At this stage of the game, it is not easy to pin down a correct definition for any of these terms.

Many digital devices are called computers or data processors. Data processors are generally used not only to compute, but also to perform other functions with data that flows to and from them. As an example, data processors are used to gather data from various sources, rearrange it, and then print the data. These operations do not use arithmetic manipulation that we usually associate with a computer, but the computer term is still applied to this application anyway. Thus, the definitions for computer and data processor have been loosely used for quite some time.

DATA PROCESSOR TERM

The definition for a data processor is a digital device that processes data. It might be a computer. But it can also be used to gather, distribute, digest, analyze and perform other data operations. These operations would not necessarily be computational. The term for data processor is narrow, while the definition for computer covers a broad field.

THE MICROPROCESSOR VERSUS THE MICROCOMPUTER

Is the definition for microprocessor and microcomputer one and the same? The answer could be yes or no, depending upon whom you are talking to at the moment.

A microcomputer or small computer is a complete working system. The small computer would contain a microprocessor chip, memory, clock, input/output (I/O) ports, power supply and other support devices. The term microprocessor therefore describes an extremely small electronic system that is capable of performing specific tasks. I am sure that in the near future a complete microcomputer will be fabricated on a single chip, including memory and I/O ports. Each day sees newer and more powerful microprocessor chips come on the market. From the preceding observations, a microprocessor is not a microcomputer, but is only a part of one.

A microprocessor, then, is the control and processing portion of a small computer or microcomputer. And it is usually referred to as the type of processor built with LSI-MOS (large-scale integration-metal-oxide semiconductor) circuitry that is usually all in one chip. Like all computer processors, microprocessors can handle both arithmetic and logic data in bit-parallel fashion under control of a program. These are both distinguished from a minicomputer processor by their use of LSI with its lower power and costs of other LSI devices by their programmable behavior.

BINARY CODES

Computer binary codes are referred to as alphanumeric codes because they are used to represent both numbers and characters. The most common codes you will hear in computer jargon are hexadecimal, ASCII and Baudot. We'll discuss two of them.

The ASCII Code

The most popular computer coding scheme is known as the American Standard Code for Information Interchange and is referred to by the letters ASCII. The letters ASCII are pronounced as-key. ASCII is a special form of binary code that is used with microprocessors and data communications systems. (Another code name that is gaining in popularity is the American National Standard Code for Information Interchange (ANSCII). ASCII is a 7-bit binary code that is used to transfer data between the microprocessor and its peripheral or I/O devices. A serial ASCII code referred to as RS232C is used for communicating data by radio and telephone. With six bits, a total of 2 to the power of 6, or 64 different characters can be represented. These characters make up decimal numbers 0 through 9, the alphabet upper-case letters, along with the other characters used for punctuation and control. The full or extended 7-bit ASCII code is represented by a total of 2 to the power of 7 or

Table 2-1. The 7-Bit ASCII Code.

COLUMN	BITS 4321	0 (3)	1 (3)	2 (3)	3	4	5	6	7 (3)
ROW	765	000	001	010	011	100	101	110	111
0	0000	NUL	DLE	SP	0	@	P	\	p
1	0001	SOH	DC1	!	1	A	Q	a	q
2	0010	STX	DC2	"	2	B	R	b	r
3	0011	ETX	DC3	#	3	C	S	c	s
4	0100	EOT	DC4	$	4	D	T	d	t
5	0101	ENQ	NAK	%	5	E	U	e	u
6	0110	ACK	SYN	&	6	F	V	f	v
7	0111	BEL	ETB	'	7	G	W	g	w
8	1000	BS	CAN	(	8	H	X	h	x
9	1001	HT	EM	)	9	I	Y	i	y
10	1010	LF	SUB	*	:	J	Z	j	z
11	1011	VT	ESC	+	;	K	[	k	{
12	1100	FF	FS	<		L		l	
13	1101	CR	GS	−	=	M	] (1)	m	}
14	1110	SO	RS	.	>	N	—(2)	n	~
15	1111	SI	US	/	?	O		o	DEL

128 different characters. The 7-bit ASCII contains lowercase letters of the alphabet and additional characters for punctuation and machine control. The 7-bit standard ASCII code is shown in the Table 2-1.

In a microcomputer, the text or information is stored as a sequence of bits (binary digits) and is referred to as a string. When the text is printed out, the bits are fetched in the proper sequence and transmitted to a video display or printer. Logic associated with the display or printer interprets the binary data of the characters it represents. If the text is entered via a keyboard, as a particular key is depressed the binary digit code associated with that key is transmitted to the microcomputer. The "micro" then stores this code in the appropriate memory bank. The standard ASCII and hexadecimal character codes are shown in Table 2-2.

Baudot Code

The Baudot code is a binary code that has five binary digits to represent a character, such as five rows of holes on punched paper tapes with each row capable of representing a single character. This Baudot code is used in standard commercial teletypewriter transmissions involving the use of punched paper tape.

The standard five-channel teletypewriter code consists of a start inpulse and five character impulses, all of equal length, and a stop impulse whose length is 1.42 times longer.

Table 2-2. Standard Character Code.

Hexadecimal Representation	ASCII (7 bit)	EBCDIC (8 bit)
0		
1		
2		
3		
4		
5		
6		
7		
8		
9		
A		
B		
C		
D		
E		
F		
10		
11		
12		
13		
14		
15		
16		
17		
18		
19		
1A		
1B		
1C		
1D		
1E		
1F		
20	blank	
21	!	
22	"	
23	#	
24	$	
25	%	
26	&	
27	'	
28	(	
29	)	
2A	*	
2B	+	
2C	'	
2D	—	
2E	.	
2F	/	
30	0	

Table 2-2 Cont. from page 36

Hexadecimal Representation	ASCII (7 bit)	EBCDIC (8 bit)
31	1	
32	2	
33	3	
34	4	
35	5	
36	6	
37	7	
38	8	
39	9	
3A	:	
3B	;	
3C	〈	
3D	=	
3E	〉	
3F	?	
40	@	blank
41	A	
42	B	
43	C	
44	D	
45	E	
46	F	
47	G	
48	H	
49	I	
4A	J	]
4B	K	.
4C	L	〈
4D	M	(
4E	N	+
4F	O	!
50	P	
51	Q	
52	R	
53	S	
54	T	
55	U	
56	V	
57	W	
58	X	
59	Y	
5A	Z	[
5B	[	$
5C	\	*
5D	]	)
5E		;
5F		∧
60		
61	a	

Table 2-2 Cont. from page 37

Hexadecimal Representation	ASCII (7 bit)	EBCDIC (8 bit)
62	b	
63	c	
64	d	
65	e	
66	f	
67	g	
68	h	
69	i	
6A	j	
6B	k	
6C	l	%
6D	m	—
6E	n	⟩
6F	o	?
70	p	
71	q	
72	r	
73	s	
74	t	
75	u	
76	v	
77	w	
78	x	
79	y	
7A	z	:
7B		#
7C		@
7D		.
7E		=
7F		"
80		
81		a
82		b
83		c
84		d
85		e
86		f
87		g
88		h
89		i
8A		
8B		
8C		
8D		
8E		
8F		
90		
91		j
92		k
93		l
94		m
95		n
96		o

Table 2-2 Cont. from page 38

Hexadecimal Representation	ASCII (7 bit)	EBCDIC (8 bit)
97		p
98		q
99		r
9A		
9B		
9C		
9D		
9E		
9F		
A0		
A1		
A2		s
A3		t
A4		u
A5		v
A6		w
A7		x
A8		y
A9		z
AA		
AB		
AC		
AD		
AE		
AF		
B0		
B1		
B2		
B3		
B4		
B5		
B6		
B7		
B8		
B9		
BA		
BB		
BC		
BD		
BE		
BF		
C0		A
C1		B
C2		C
C3		D
C4		E
C5		F
C6		G
C7		H
C8		I
C9		
CA		
CB		

Table 2-2 Cont. from page 39

Hexadecimal Representation	ASCII (7 bit)	EBCDIC (8 bit)
CC		
CD		
CE		
CF		
D0		
D1		J
D2		K
D3		L
D4		M
D5		N
D6		O
D7		P
D8		Q
D9		R
DA		
DB		
DC		
DD		
DE		
DF		
E0		
E1		
E2		S
E3		T
E4		U
E5		V
E6		W
E7		X
E8		Y
E9		Z
EA		
EB		
EC		
ED		
EE		
EF		
F0		0
F1		1
F2		2
F3		3
F4		4
F5		5
F6		6
F7		7
F8		8
F9		9
FA		
FB		
FC		
FD		
FE		
FF		

SYSTEM INTERFACING

Interfacing can be defined as joining a group of devices so they work in a compatible manner, including memory and I/O ports. Some terms used with interfacing are as follows:

- Synchronous or sync—in step or in phase, as for two devices. For a computer this would be a performance of a sequence of operations as controlled by clock signals or pulses.
- Synchronous operation—system operation under the control of clock pulses.
- Synchronous logic—type of digital logic used in a system in which logical operations take place in synchronism with clock pulses.
- To synchronize or sync in—to lock one element of a system into step with another.
- Sync pulses—pulses developed at transmitting equipment and introduced into the receiving equipment to keep both systems operating in step.
- Synchronous inputs—those inputs of a flip-flop that do not control the output directly, as do those of a gate, but only when the clock permits and commands.

Although the details of computer interfacing vary with the type of microcomputer used, the general principles of interfacing apply to

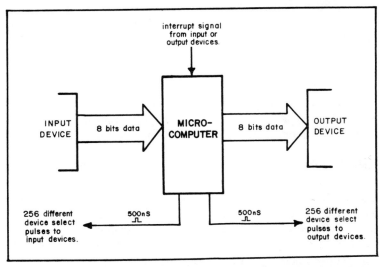

Fig. 2-1. The four principle tasks of interfacing: input, output, device select pulse generation and interrupt servicing.

a wide variety of microcomputers. For the 8080A microprocessor, the basic objectives of interfacing are summarized in Fig. 2-1.

The objectives of microcomputer interfacing are as follows:

■ Synchronize the transfer of 8 bit of data between each input device and the microcomputer.

■ Synchronize the transfer of 8 bits of data between the microcomputer and each output device.

■ Generate the appropriate input and output data transfer sync pulses, which are called device select pulses. For an 8080A-based microcomputer, 256 different input sync pulses and 256 different output sync pulses can be generated.

■ Service interrupt signals that enter the microcomputer from external I/O devices.

■ Program the microcomputer to perform all input and interrupt servicing operations.

Interface Busses

The block diagram in Fig. 2-2 gives you another view for three of these interfacing busses. Briefly, the transfer of 8-bits of data between the CPU and an I/O device occurs over the 8-bit bidirectional data bus. The specific I/O device that is involved in the data transfer is selected Via the use of 8-bits on the address bus. The precise timing of the data transfer is determined by the presence of an IN or OUT pulse on the control bus. Thus, during the transfer of data between the CPU and I/O device, all three busses are participating.

INPUT/OUTPUT DEVICES

What is an I/O device, you may ask? It is any digital device, including a single integrated circuit chip, that transmits data to, or receives data or strobe pulses from, a microcomputer.

Usually you would think of an I/O device as a large, complex unit. Some of these large I/O devices are CRT terminals, card readers, modems and line printers. However, a single IC chip, such as a latch, tri-state buffer, shift register, or small memory, can be classified as an I/O device.

The transfer of data between a microcomputer and an I/O device must be synchronized, and this is accomplished with pulses called device select pulses. We should point out that several device select pulses may be required for a single I/O device. In one example, a 74198 shift register has a pair of control inputs that

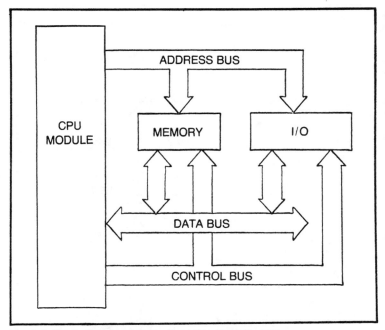

Fig. 2-2. Block diagram showing three interfacing busses.

determine whether the register shifts left or right, or parallel loads eight bits of data. The chip also contains clock and clear inputs. Thus, a single 74198 chip may require three or four unique device select pulses. You can generate 256 different input device select pulses and 256 different output device select pulses, but this does not mean that you can address 512 different devices. A more reasonable number is somewhere between 50 and 100 devices. Rarely would you need this many device select pulses. If need be, design changes can be made to generate more select pulses.

Interface Switches and Contact Bounce

When data is sent into the microprocessor via keyboard or microswitches, these undebounced pulses will give spurious spikes when changing from one logic state to another. Keyboard interfacing switches are shown in Fig. 2-3. The spurious pulses—note waveform shown in Fig. 2-4—are a consequence of contact bounce at the switch contacts. Just about all switches produce contact bounce. When the switch is closed, the contacts do not make a positive electrical or mechanical connection, but bounce open and closed for a short period of time.

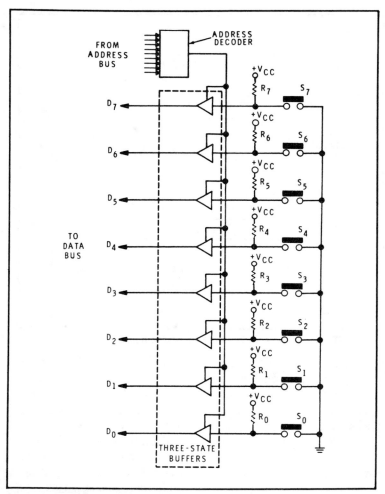

Fig. 2-3. Keyboard interfacing switches.

Microswitches and rotary switches all exhibit contact bounce when changed from position to position. The closing of a switch is not an action that can be accomplished in a few microseconds. It occurs over a period of milliseconds to hundreds of millseconds. Thus, it is just the nature of mechanical switches that they will bounce. Contact bounce may only last for a few milliseconds, but that is long enough for the MPU (microprocessing unit) to believe that the bounces are also switch contact closures. To solve this contact bounce problem, some switches use cross-coupled NAND gates that instantly latch onto one state, which ignores all contact bounce. Of course, this will require some additional circuitry.

A much better design scheme would be to let the MPU itself do the debouncing. A technique that is often used is to wait about ten milliseconds and then read the data from the switchbank again. If the same data is read, then the MPU can be certain that the switch is closed. The switch contacts can be checked or poled as many times as required until contact bounce is eliminated. Always keep these points in mind and be on the alert for contact bounce which could cause glitches in the program that give false information during microcomputer system troubleshooting.

THE INTEL 8080A MICROPROCESSOR

The 8080A is a complete 8-bit central processing unit (CPU). This N-channel microprocessor is fabricated on a single large-scale integrated (LSI) chip. The 8080A has many control and processing applications. In order for you to visualize the complexity of this micro, a magnified photo of this chip is shown in Fig. 2-9.

The 8080A contains six 8-bit general purpose working registers and an accumulator. Note the functional CPU block diagram in Fig. 2-6. The six general-purpose registers may be addressed individually or in pairs providing both single and double precision operators. Arithmetic and logical instructions set or reset four testable flags. A fifth flag provides decimal arithmetic operations.

There is also an external stack feature wherein any portion of memory may be used as a last in/first out stack to store or retrieve the contents of the accumulator, flags, program counter and all the six general-purpose registers. The 16 bit stack pointer controls the addressing of this external stack. This stack gives the 8080A the ability to easily handle multiple-level priority interrupts by rapidly storing and restoring processor status. It also provides almost unlimited subroutine nesting.

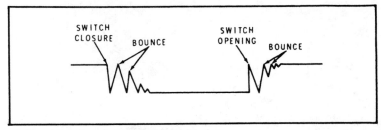

Fig. 2-4. Waveform caused by contact bounce.

Fig. 2-5. Magnified photograph of the 8080A microprocessor chip by Intel.

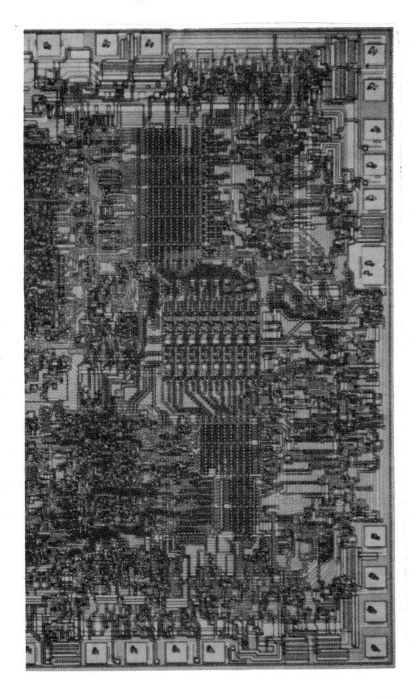

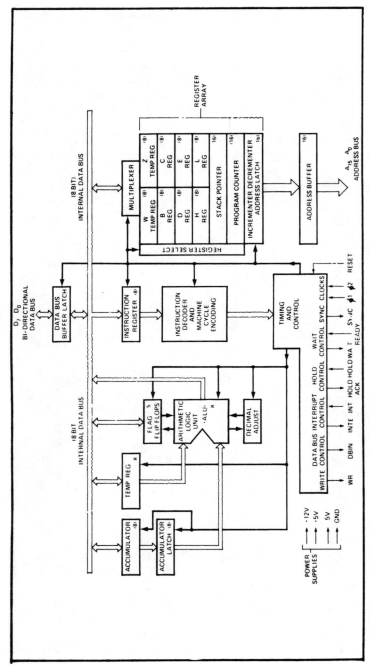

Fig. 2-6. Functional block diagram of the Intel 8080A CPU.

This microprocessor chip has been designed to simplify the complete systems design of the computer. Separate 16-line address and 8-line bidirectional data busses are used to facilitate easy interface to memory and I/O. Signals to controls the interface to memory and I/O are provided directly by the 8080A. Ultimate control of the address and data busses resides with the HOLD signal. It provides the ability to suspend processor operation and force the address and data busses into a high-impedance state. This permits OR—typing these busses with other controlling devices for direct memory access (DMA) or multiprocessor operation.

Some 8080A Chip Requirements

The simple block diagram of the 8080A microprocessor chip is shown in Fig. 2-7. A typical microcomputer designed from an 8080A chip possesses all of the minimum requirements for a digital computer, which are as follows:

- It is programmable, with the data and program instructions capable of being arranged in any sequence desired.
- It is digital.
- It is clocked (in most microcomputers, the internal operations in the CPU chip proceed synchronously).

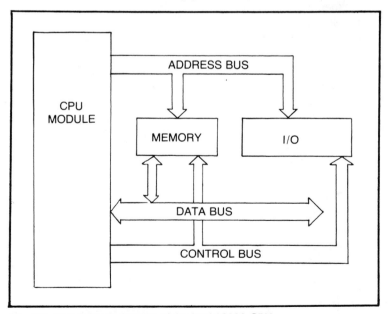

Fig. 2-7. Simple block diagram of the Intel 8080A CPU.

- It contains an arithmetic/logic unit located within the CPU chip, that performs arithmetric and logic operations.
- It can exchange data with memory or I/O devices.
- It contains fast memory. Speed is an important requirement for a functional digital computer.

Address Bus for the 8080A Micro Chip

The 8080A micro chip has a 16-bit address bus that is used for identification of specific memory locations or specific I/O devices. This is an unidirectional bus, with only address information coming out of the 8080A chip. When addressed, 65,536 different memory locations can be accessed. The 8080A is a 64K device, where the K indicates kilobyte, or 1024 bytes.

The address bus is also used to supply the 8-bit device code for input and output devices. When addressing input-output devices, the address bus will assume another identity. Thus, it is subdivided into two identical 8-bit device code bytes, which are used as interface circuits to I/O devices. When addressing I/O devices using the IN or OUT microcomputer instructions, 256 different input and output devices can be addressed.

When working on a bus problem, you should be aware of the possibility that different types of information appear on the bus line at different times. This is the case with the 8080A address bus system. Most of the time the information that appears on the address BUS is the address of a specific memory location. Occasionally, the information that appears on the address BUS is a device code. The microcomputer knows when the BUS is being used to access memory and when it is being used to identify I/O devices, as it provides the appropriate control pulse which informs you what it is doing. Always keep these control pulses in mind when troubleshooting these bus systems.

Bidirectional Data Bus

The 8080A chip contains an 8-bit bidirectional data bus that permits eight bits of data, known as a byte, to be transferred between the micro chip and memory or I/O device. Much of the time, data that appears on the data bus is an instruction byte from memory. At other times, the data that appears on the data bus is one of the following:

- A data byte that is being input from an input device.
- A data byte that is being output to an output device.

- A data byte that is being written into or read from memory.
- Control status bits used to derive some of the control bus signals.
- A HI or LO address byte that is being stored in an area of memory called the stack.
- A HI or LO address byte that is being retrieved from the stack.
- An instruction byte that is being jammed by an I/O device during an interrupt.

The microprocessor provides the appropriate control or status pulses that inform you about the type of activity currently in progress.

FLOWCHARTS

A flowchart is a schematic diagram for the flow of information through the various components that make up the microprocessor system. This flowchart can be used as a map by the technician when troubleshooting systems that can be quite complex. As the systems program is being developed and debugged, the design engineer will usually draw a flowchart. Many times the flowchart will be drawn before any program is written. The flowchart is a most important way of documenting an operational program. The chart in Fig. 2-8 shows some of the more common or standard flow diagram symbols. These symbols are used to distinguish the various classes of

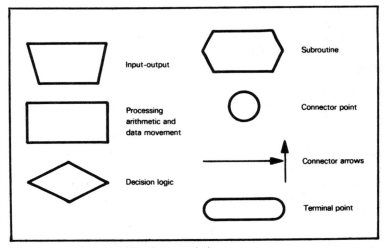

Fig. 2-8. Some standard flowchart symbols.

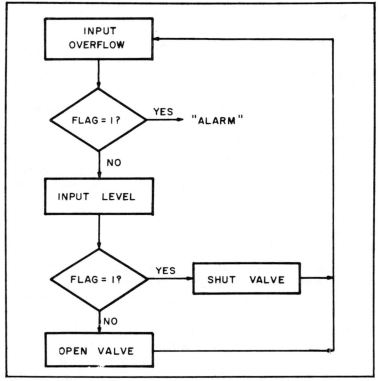

Fig. 2-9. A system flow chart for controlling the level of a liquid in a storage tank.

operation from input to output of the system. As an example of how these symbols are used, Fig. 2-9 shows a system flowchart for controlling the level of solvent in a storage tank.

MINICOMPUTER SPEECH ENTRY APPLICATIONS

Data entry into the home microcomputer via the human voice is now possible on a limited scale at low cost. In the next few years, a technological breakthrough is a certainty. Of course, Bell Laboratories and Carnegie-Mellon university are developing new ideas each day in regards to voice input to computers and related knowledge of voice patterns or speech recognition. Also, the high density and low cost of the bubble magnetic memories now coming on stream will greatly increase the vocabulary of these speech recognition systems.

One voice control unit, now available at a low cost for the home microcomputer is the Speechlab system by Heuristics, Inc. of Los

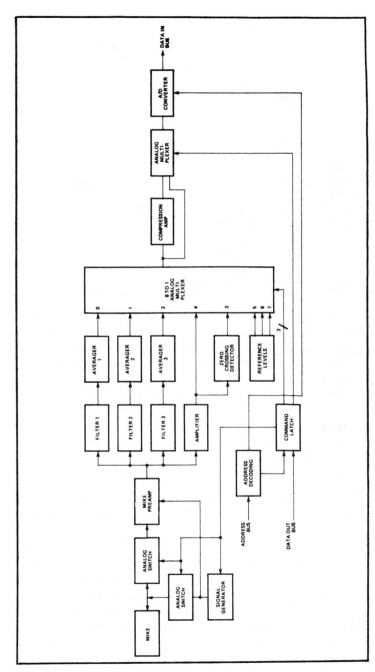

Fig. 2-10. Block diagram of the SpeechLab model 50 speed recognition peripheral.

53

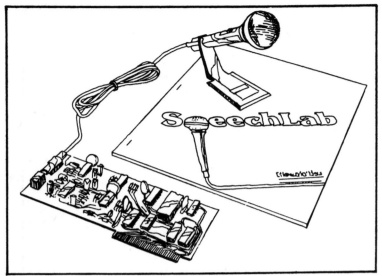

Fig. 2-11. The model 20A by SpeechLab speech recognition peripheral.

Altos, CA. The Speechlab system can be plugged into any microcomputer, with an S-100 bus and will directly control the various programs. Some of the computer brand names are SOL, Vector-Graphics, Altair, Imsai, Byte, Inc. and many others. Also, it can be adapted for use with other computer systems. The assembled Speechlab comes with a complete hardware system, including a high fidelity microphone. The PC (printed circuit) board unit is ready to plug into the S-100 bus of the computer to start someone on voice control programs. Also included is a complete hardware and Speechlab Laboratory manual.

Let's now take a brief review of this speech system's technical features. The Speechlab offers 64 bytes of storage for each spoken word, has real time response, and is 95-percent correct in its recognition. The system is capable of handling a 64-word vocabulary, and also features the latest CMOS design for reliability and low power consumption. Typical power consumption is about 1 watt.

The Speechlab system features functional signal processing modules so that they can be reconfigured under software control for maximum freedom. Filter skirt rolloff is 80 db per decade. The unit also has a signal generator for prompting and built-in tests that are usually only found in more expensive equipment. Another feature is the single input/output port. A block diagram of the model 50 Speechlab system is shown in Fig. 2-10.

Hardware includes three band-pass filters (6 bits amplitude), one zero crossing detector, a linear amplifier, compression amplifier, 6-bit A/D converter and a beeper. The raw waveform is available for advanced experiments.

Software includes seven complete programs, three of which are offered in source and on paper tape and four in source alone. The ones on paper tape and source include a Speech Basic programming language, an assembly language speech recognition program and a hardware self-test program. Source programs are a Speech Basic plot, a Speech Basic correlation, a Speech Basic recognition and a Speech Basic advanced recognition.

The Speechlab model 20 shown in Fig. 2-11 has a vocabulary of 32 words. The model 20S is used in computers with the S-100 bus. The model 20A works with the Apple II small computer system. The model 20 features ROM based software with a relocatable program which lets you load anywhere into memory with a vacant spot. After loading, the 2K ROM can be disabled under computer control. The speech recognition program, callable from any BASIC, requires 4K bytes of user-supplied RAM. This RAM can be located anywhere in the address space. Model 20 hardware includes two band-pass filters with 2 bits of amplitude, two zero crossing detectors and a linear amplifier. The Speechlab model 50 that plugs into a

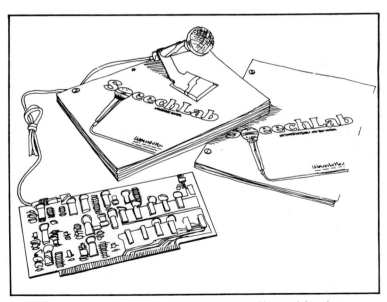

Fig. 2-12. The SpeechLab model 50 speech recognition peripheral.

S-100 bus computer system, such as a SOL-20, is shown in the Fig. 2-12.

SPEECHLAB MODEL 20 HARDWARE OPERATION

The SpeechLab model 20 hardware consists of a microphone amplifier with frequency compensation, two analog band-pass filters, each with a signal rectification/averaging stage, a zero crossing detector, a 1K byte ROM and logic to run the input port and the ROM memory interface. Figure 2-13 shows a block diagram of the model 20, Fig. 2-14 shows a schematic diagram of the circuit.

Microphone Preamp

The first element in the signal chain is the microphone, which produces an analog signal on the order of 10 millivolts for normal speech. The first stage of the microphone preamp preemphasizes signals up to 3.1 kHz at a rate of 6 dB per octave. That is, high-frequency signals are amplified more than low-frequency signals, with the rate of gain increase being a factor of two for each doubling in frequency up to 3.1 kHz. From 3.1 kHz to 6.6 kHz, the gain of the amplifier is constant, and the gain drops off beyond 6.6 kHz at the rate of 6 db per octave. This preemphasis compensates for the characteristics of the human vocal tract, which produces less energy in the higher audio frequency ranges than in the lower frequencies. The preemphasis tends to make all frequency components have the same order of magnitude. The output of the first stage feeds the second stage, which simply amplifies the first stage output by a factor of 60. The microphone preamp output is biased such that the output rests at about 5.5 volts with no signal into the preamp, and swings about this reference voltage by ±5.5 volts, utilizing the full dynamic range of 0 to 11 volts.

Filters

The output of the microphone preamp feeds two audio band-pass filters. These filters amplify and extract that portion of the speech utterance which falls within the frequency bandpass of the filter. The first filter has a frequency bandpass range of 150 Hz to 900 Hz; the second filter ranges from 900 Hz to 5 kHz. The lower frequency band corresponds to the frequency range of the lowest frequency resonance (formant) of the human vocal tract, and the higher frequency band corresponds to the frequency band of the next two vocal tract resonances. The energy and frequency in each

56

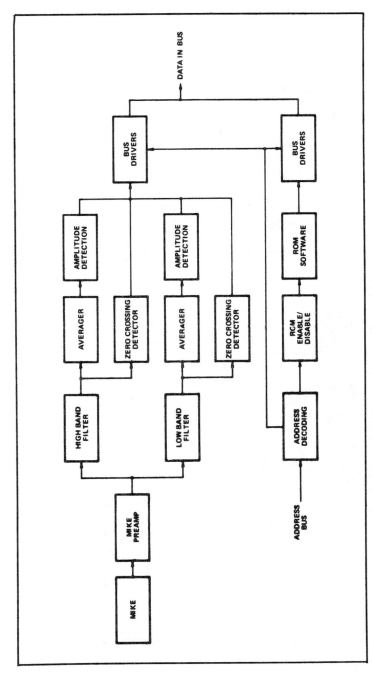

Fig. 2-13. Block diagram of the SpeechLab model 20A speech recognition peripheral.

57

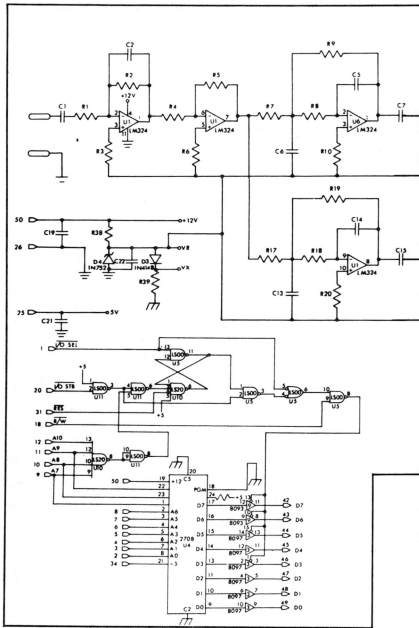

Fig. 2-14. Circuit diagram of the SpeechLab model 20A speech recognition peripheral.

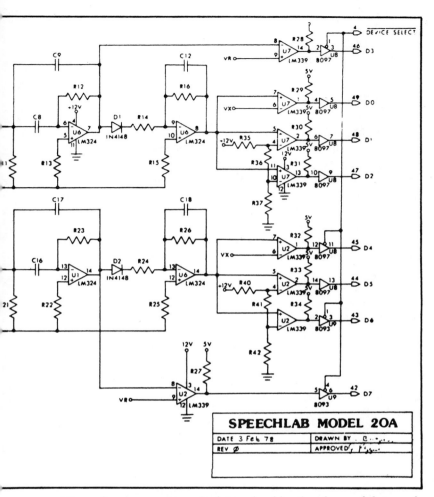

SPEECHLAB MODEL 20A

DATE 3 Feb 78	DRAWN BY . C . . . . .
REV Ø	APPROVED , ...

of these frequency ranges is determined by the shape of the vocal tract which, of course, varies with time to produce time-varying outputs from these filters during a speech utterance.

The band-pass filters are each implemented as a cascade of a second-degree multiple feedback low-pass filter followed by a second-degree multiple feedback high-pass filter to yield attenuations of 40 db/decade (12 db/octave) above and below the pass bands. The outputs of each filter are biased to the reference level of 5.5 volts. That is, in the absence of any signal, the output will rest at 5.5 volts, and in the presence of a signal will swing above and below that level. Each filter output produces sine waves proportional in

59

amplitude and equal in frequency to the output of the microphone signal that falls within the frequency bandpass of the filter. The output of each filter is fed to a zero crossing detector and a rectifier/averager.

Zero Crossing Detector

The zero crossing detectors provide a means of measuring the dominant frequency component of the signal passing through each of the filters. The zero crossing detector is a comparator with one input connected to the reference voltage and the other input connected to the filter output. Because the filter output is equal to the reference voltage (5.5 V) when no signal is input to the microphone, the two comparator inputs are equal when no signal is present. When a signal is present, however, the output of the filter will swing above and below the reference voltage. When the filter output is above the reference voltage, the comparator will be forced to a logic zero output. When the filter output is below the reference voltage, the comparator is forced to a logic one state. Every time the filter output crosses the reference voltage, the comparator changes state. The output of each comparator is connected to the parallel output port, where they can be input to the computer. The computer reads the zero crossing detectors and determines the number of times the comparator changes state, from one to zero or vice versa, in a given time period. This number is equal to the number of times the filter output crosses the reference voltage level. If the input to the filter were a single sine wave, the number of state changes in one second would be exactly twice the frequency, because a sine wave crosses the reference voltage twice in one period. Speech waveforms typically have several frequencies present with one frequency dominant. The dominant frequency in a frequency range is equal to the resonant frequency of the vocal tract in that frequency range. The other frequencies are attenuated by the vocal tract. The addition of small amplitude waves on the dominant wave causes sinusoidal ripples in the dominant wave. These ripples sometimes occur as the dominant wave passes through the reference voltage level at the output of the filter, producing additional zero crossings compared to the number produced by the dominant wave alone. The difference, though, is small and of little consequence. The output of the filter is also fed to a rectifier/average stage.

Rectifier/Averager

The rectifier/averager circuit produces an output proportional to the amplitude of the sine waves coming from its associated filter.

This is accomplished by rectifying the filter output relative to the reference voltage and time averaging the result. The rectification is implemented with a diode, which only passes current to the averager when the filter output is above the reference voltage. The time averager is a low-pass filter (leaky memory) with a bandwidth of 20 Hz. In the absence of new signals from the filter, the averager will decay to its no-signal value, the reference voltage, with a time constant of 50 milliseconds. Thus the averager forgets events which occurred 50 milliseconds in the past. The output of the averager is a voltage proportional to the energy of the waveform from its associated filter. The output of the rectifier/averager is fed to the amplitude detection hardware.

Amplitude Detection

Amplitude detection is simply accomplished by comparing the output of the rectifier/averager stage with three fixed voltages using three voltage comparators. One of the comparator reference voltages is set very close to the no-signal output of the rectifier/averager to determine the beginning and ending of words. The other two reference voltages are set at about one-third and two-thirds of the dynamic range of the rectifier/averager outputs. These comparator outputs, three for each of the two frequency bands, are routed to the parallel input port where they can be input to the computer.

ROM Enable/Disable

The ROM enable/disable circuitry operates in accordance with the rules for Apple II computer peripherals with on-board ROM. The I/O select signal from board connector pin 1 enables the on-board ROM whenever the processor executes a memory read instruction to read from the 256-byte block of memory set aside for each peripheral card. This address block is CN00 to CNFF where N is the peripheral connector slot number, 1 to 7. Once a memory read instruction from this address block has occurred, an RS flip-flop is set to enable mode, which allows the on-board 1K-byte ROM to occupy half of the full 2K-byte address space from C800H to CFFFH set aside for any peripheral. This range is detected via the I/O strobe signal which decodes this address range on the Apple II mainframe. The ROM will remain enabled until a memory access is made to the address range CF80H to CFFFH, or until a reset occurs, whichever happens first.

Chapter 3
The Microprocessor
and Its Support Device

For a simple explanation of what is a microprocessor, we can use Fig. 3-1, which shows a person who has a machine that is needed for a task of some sort. If the task is as simple as turning on a light, the person must control the machine (flip a switch).

Please note that the control information is all in one direction—from left to right. Also, if the task contains many steps or procedures, the person must remember the entire sequence to perform the operation completely.

Figure 3-2 shows the process of information flow in a microprocessor system. Again the microprocessor receives a command from an input device which may or may not be controlled by a person. However, for sequenced operations we take the memory requirement away from the person and transfer it to the memory, which is part of the system. The input command may be only a signal, a pulse, caused by pushing a start button, whereas the output could be a complete series of actions whose codes are stored in memory. These codes are referred to as the *program*. Determining or setting up these codes is referred to as programming.

What does the microprocessor chip actually do? In reality, it can do anything that the input device or memory tells it to do. To keep this easy to understand, we can divide all the microprocessor activities into two categories:

■ It routes data output from input or memory to output or memory. This is simply a movement of data from one

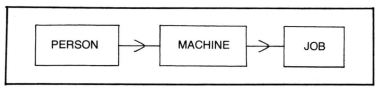

Fig. 3-1. Block diagram of a simple microprocessor operation.

place to another, somewhat like a large multipole, multiposition switch.

■ It performs operations on data, operations such as algebraic addition and subtraction, comparison of two numbers, and even some simple logical decision making, such as branching in a flow chart. We can see a micro chip has two sections of circuitry: a control section, which takes care of housekeeping details of data routing; and an arithmetic-logic-unit (ALU) to perform the various operations.

BUSSES

To get information to and from the mircoprocessor brain or CPU, a system of address, control and data busses are required. These busses, as they are referred to in computer jargon, are a group of conductors over which bits of data are transferred to and from various points in the system. Some are bidirectional busses, which means that information can be transferred in both directions. Generally, only one transfer of data can occur at one time for each bus. Some of the more sophisticated systems use a time-sharing or bit-slicing technique which enables more than one data transfer at a time. In addition to microprocessors, many logic designed devices use time-sharing on a single lead wire.

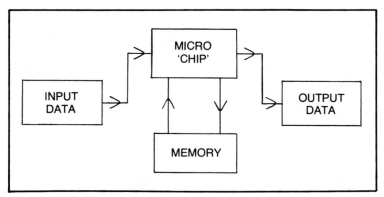

Fig. 3-2. Block diagram of a micro system.

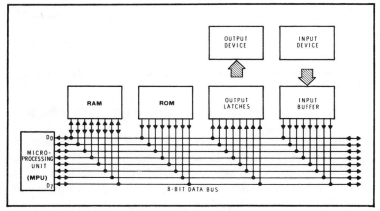

Fig. 3-3. Typical data bus arrangement.

Running the Bus Lines

A digital bus is a path over which digital information is transferred from any of several sources to any of several destinations. Only one transfer of information can take place at any one time. While such a transfer is taking place, all other sources that are tied to the bus must be disabled. The verb, *to bus*, means to interconnect several digital devices, which either receive or transmit digital information, by a common set of conducting paths, called a bus, over which all information between such devices is transferred.

The basic purpose of a bus is to minimize the number of interconnections required to transfer information between digital devices. Busses are present within IC chips, such as the 8080A microprocessor; between IC chips as with the address, control, and bidirectional data busses present in the 8080A; and between digital systems and instruments.

The concept of a bus is probably one of the most important concepts in digital electronics. Without the ability to share information paths, most digital devices would require three or four times the number of wire connectors that are now needed. Printed circuit boards for microcomputers would be considerably more complex... and expensive.

Figure 3-3 shows a simple data bus setup for a microcomputer. In this system all data transfers are via the MPU. Note that data can be moved in either direction between the RAM and the MPU. All other data moves in one direction only. Data can be moved from the ROM or input buffer to the MPU. And data can be sent from the MPU via latches to the outside world.

To fetch and retrieve data transfers properly (in this case, only one at a time) an address bus must be added to the system. Each data source is then assigned a different address. As an example, the RAM, ROM, input buffers, and output latches all have chip enable pins. The correct logic pulse at these pins will activate or enable the circuit. With a different address for each circuit, then only one circuit will function at any given point in time. The address bus is shown in Fig. 3-4, a block diagram of a micro system.

In this micro system, inputs to the address decoders come from the MPU via the address bus. And the outputs go to the chip enable lines of these various circuits. Only one address can appear on the address bus at any one point in time, thereby enabling only one external circuit at a time.

Just as each home has its mailing address, so must each byte have its assigned address. When any one of these addresses appear on the address bus, the RAM is selected via its chip enable line. Note that part of the address bus connects directly to the RAM, which selects the individual byte within the RAM chip.

ROM is also assigned a range of addresses that must be enabled when any of these addresses appear on the address bus. The output latch and input buffers are also assigned specific addresses. In this way, the MPU can "talk to" any of the external circuits just by putting the correct address on the address bus.

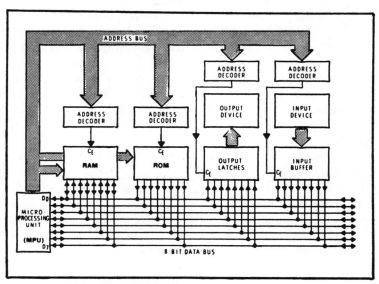

Fig. 3-4. Addition of the address bus.

There is another problem because of the nature of two-state digital logic circuits. Regardless of which of the two states they are in, the circuits interfere with output of the enable circuit. For example, if the output of the disabled circuits assumes a high state, this will then interfere with a low output of an enabled circuit. Thus, you will have a condition where one circuit tries to pull the bus high while the other one is trying to go low. A tri-state device is usually used in microprocessors to overcome this problem.

TRI-STATE LOGIC

A tri-state logic device has a third state in addition to the logic 1 and logic 0 states. Figure 3-5 illustrates the common noninverting buffer along with the tri-state, noninverting buffer.

The noninverting buffer increases the current drive of the input signal without altering the logic levels. For this reason, the output could drive 10 times as many gates as the input. The common buffer has one input and one output. The output always has the same logic levels as the input. Thus, the input must be either 1 or 0. And the output must follow the same logic.

However, the tri-state buffer has two inputs. Along with the normal data input, the buffer has an enable/disable input. The input can be either a logic 1 or logic 0, depending on whether the buffer is to be enabled or disabled. The tri-state buffer in Fig. 3-5B is enabled by applying logic 1 to the enable/disable input.

This unique tri-state concept allows outputs to be tied together and then connected to a common bus line. Normal TTL outputs cannot be connected because of the low-impedance logical "1" output current which one device would have to sink from the other. If, however, both the upper and lower output transistors are turned off on all but one of the connected devices, then the one remaining device in the normal low-impedance state will have only a small amount of leakage current to supply to, or sink from, the other devices.

It is true that in a TTL system, open-collector gates could be used to perform the logic functions of these tri-state elements, but neither waveform integrity nor optimum speed would be obtained. The low-output impedance of tri-state devices provides good capacitance drive capability and rapid transition from the logical "0" to logical "1" level, thus assuring both speed and waveform integrity. It is possible to connect as many as 128 devices to a common bus line and still have adequate drive capability to allow fan-out from the bus.

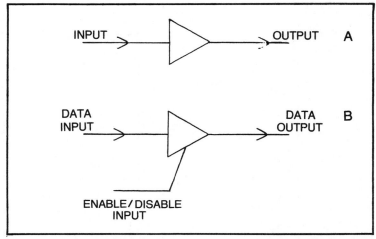

Fig. 3-5. Common noninverting buffer at (A) and tri-state noninverting buffer at (B).

Another advantage of tri-state buffers is that in the high-impedance state, their inputs do not present the normal loading to the driving device. This is significant when it is desirable to transmit in both directions over a common line. In summation, a tri-state device has three possible output states:

■ A logical "0" state.
■ A logical "1" state.
■ A high-impedance output state that is, in effect, disconnected from the bus line.

All three-state devices have an input pin called an enable/disable input, which permits the logic devices either to behave normally or to exist in the high-impedance state. When enabled, a tri-state device behaves as a normal TTL device. When disabled, a tri-state device behaves as if it is, in effect, disconnected from the circuit.

SIMPLE BUS SYSTEM EXAMPLES

As we look at Fig. 3-6, you will see a simple four-device one-line bus system that is based upon the use of a single 74126 three-state buffer chip. You can tell this is a bus system since the outputs of gates A through D are connected together. With standard 7400-series TTL chips, you could not use this is a bus system unless the chips have special output circuits—either three-state or open collector—that permit bussing.

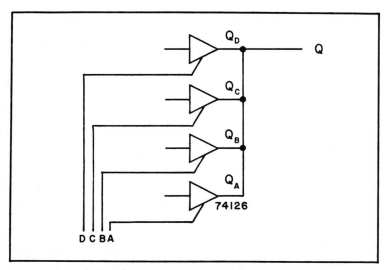

Fig. 3-6. A simple four-device one-line bus based upon the use of four 74126 tri-state buffers.

If we assume that gates A through D in Fig. 3-6 are enabled by a logic "1" input, the operation of the circuit should be clear. Only one buffer gate may be enabled at any instant of time, and the remaining buffer gates must be disabled. Thus, digital information from only one of the four buffers appears on the single-line bus at any given time. Information from the remaining three buffers is blocked because the corresponding buffers are disabled.

Typical bus systems consist of multiline busses, as shown in Fig. 3-7, rather than just single-line busses. Other than the fact that the gating inputs enable or disable four buffer gates at a time, this circuit is identical to that shown in Fig. 3-6 for a one-line bus.

DATA STORAGE

In order to operate and function, a microprocessor or computer must have a program. And this program must be stored in a memory device. Stored in these memory devices are data and complete instruction steps for each of the microprocessors that function. These are addressable memories that send out and receive bit patterns to store and retrieve data in these memory banks. These instructions are seen by the microprocessor as binary codes in memory and are fetched out in eight-bit (a byte) chunks.

Some types of memories are read-only memory (ROM), read-write memory (RWM) and random-access memory (RAM).

ROM is used to store program steps in dedicated micro systems. Read-write memory is used to store data that changes during program operations. Random-access memory lets the microprocessor read and write from it and allows data to be stored while the program is in progress. Let's take a more detailed look at these various memory families.

The Read-Only Memory System

In order to run their programs, all micro systems must have read-only memory devices. And usually, dedicated micros will use only ROMs. To refresh your memory, ROM is an acronym for read-only memory. ROM is then a permanent memory and is nonvolatile. Its contents will therefore be unaltered with power loss or system operation error. In most cases ROMs have a random access feature. The micro cannot change the contents in the ROM, but can only read what has been stored.

A typical memory IC contains over 4,000 flip-flops, stored charges, or diodes programmed in an array of 512×8 bits. Refer to Fig. 3-8. Each memory cell (a bit) is programmed to yield a logic "1" or "0" output. Each row of 8 bits is called a byte, or can be referred to as a word. When a particular byte is addressed by the micro chip, the memory IC provides eight outputs stored in that byte on eight parallel data lines that are called the data bus.

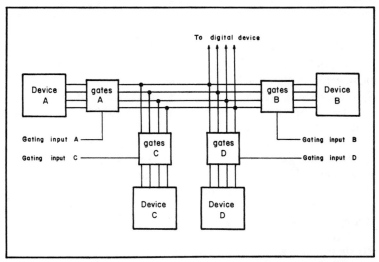

Fig. 3-7. A simple multiline bus arrangement. In this case, there are four devices and four-line busses.

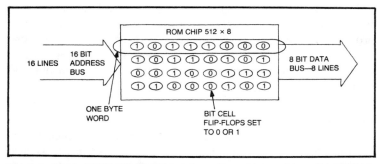

Fig. 3-8. A typical ROM IC. The data information addressed from the ROM IC chip is fed into the microprocessor to perform a specific task.

The ROM is usually programmed by changing the mask when the IC is fabricated. A PROM (programmable read-only memory) can be programmed by the user before it is inserted into the system. Generally, this type of ROM uses fusible links which can be modified by the user. Then there is the EPROM (erasable PROM), which is also programmed by the user, but can be erased by subjecting it to an ultraviolet light. After erasure, the EPROM can be reprogrammed with a new program if it is removed from the system.

A new INTEL 8355 ROM device with I/O is shown in Fig. 3-9. The ROM portion is organized as 2048 × 8, or 16,384 bits of memory. It has a maximum access time of 400 microseconds.

The Random-Access Memory System (RAM)

The RAM (random-access memory) is a device into which the micro can write data and from which the micro can read data while it is in the system. This is also referred to as read-write memory.

The RAM is a semiconductor memory into which a logic "0" or logic "1" state can be written (stored) and then read out again or retrieved. *Random* means that we can access any one of the memory locations by applying the proper logic states to the memory select inputs. Thus, we don't have to sequence through the memory in order to access a memory location. Simply stated, RAM differs from ROM in that the micro can read from and write into it, storing data while the program is operating. Most micro systems will have both ROM and RAM devices. Technically speaking, ROMs can also be called RAMs.

RAMs are divided into two types: static and dynamic. The static RAM stores each bit in a flip-flop stage. The dynamic RAM stores the data as capacitive charges. However, for dynamic RAMs an operator must periodically access these word bits in order to refresh the charges, lest the memory would fade away like an old soldier.

The dynamic RAM can store a lot more data in a given space as compared to a static memory. The dynamic RAM is much faster than the static one and consumes less power for each state change.

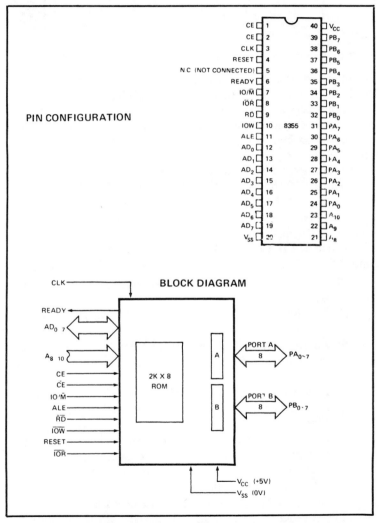

Fig. 3-9. The INTEL 8355, a 16,384-bit ROM with I/O (courtesy of INTEL).

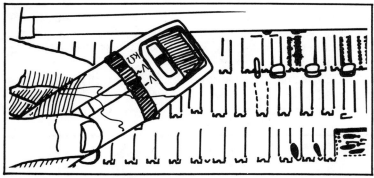

Fig. 3-10. A technician checking a RAM board with a digital voltmeter.

However, additional refresh circuitry is required for a dynamic RAM, and for many chips this is out-boarded. The term *refresh,* or *renew,* means to sequence among several states so rapidly that the digital circuit memory cannot detect that the states are being sequenced. *Refresh* implies that the same information is applied to each state, respectively, on every sequence cycle. Refresh is required so that data stored in the RAM will not be lost.

Figure 3-10 shows a technician checking a RAM board with a digital voltmeter. This is a 16K RAM memory board that plugs into a S-100 bus that is used in a SOL-20 microcomputer system built by Processor Technology Corp.

Static RAM Control Lines. Refer to Fig. 3-11. Several control lines are required for a static RAM, and they include:

■ Data out—This is a single line to output a certain bit to be addressed.

■ Data in—A single line is used to input the particular bit to be placed in memory.

■ Address lines—The number of address lines depends on the size of the RAM. A 1024-bit RAM needs 10 address lines.

■ Read-write—This is a single line with which the command to read (output) or write (input) is fed to the microprocessors.

■ Chip select or enable—Again a single line is used to disconnect the memory from the output data bus, to inhibit the *WRITE* circuitry in the chip and to control accessing of the chip.

Dynamic RAM Control Lines. Refer to Fig. 3-12. The control lines required for a dynamic RAM chip are the following:

72

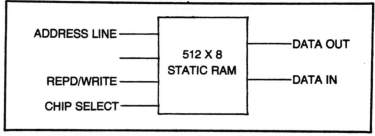

Fig. 3-11. Static RAM input and output lines.

■ Data out lines—The number of these lines required depends on RAM chip storage word size.

■ Data lines in—The number of these lines required depends on word size in the RAM chip.

■ Address lines—The number of address lines required depends on the number of words the RAM can store.

■ Chip select or enable—This line is used to control input and output from the memory. One pulse on this line is required for each READ or WRITE cycle.

■ Read-Write—The command to READ (output) or WRITE (input) is given over this line. The line is usually held in the READ state.

■ Precharge—This line must be pulsed before the output line is read so as to charge the output capacitors. This pulse timing in relation to chip select pulse is critical.

Static MOS RAM

One of the storage units for a MOS-type static RAM is shown in Fig. 3-13. Many of these units are in a typical MOS RAM, along

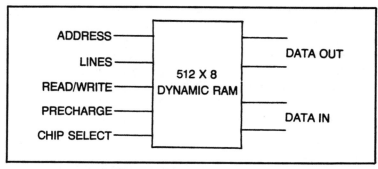

Fig. 3-12. Dynamic RAM input and output lines.

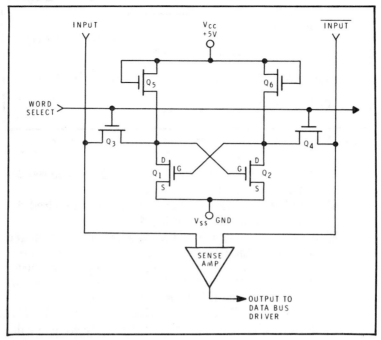

Fig. 3-13. MOS static RAM storage unit.

with bus drivers and address decoders. The storage unit contains six MOS transistors. These N-channel devices can be made to conduct by feeding a positive voltage to the gate terminal: therefore, when the gate is close to ground potential, the transistor is off and has a very high impedance. Now, when the gate goes high the transistor conducts and has a good bit lower impedance. By this action "1" and "0" are stored in these units.

INTEL's 5101 family of static CMOS RAMs is shown in Fig. 3-14. These RAMs use fully DC stable (static) circuitry, and it is not necessary to pulse the chip select for each address transition. The data is read out nondestructively and has the same polarity as the input data. The 5101 has separate data input and data output terminals. An output disable function is provided so that the data inputs and outputs may be WIRE-OR-ed for use in common data I/O systems.

THE CLOCK AND ITS OPERATION

The clock is the heart of most logic devices, because it moves the system in an orderly fashion and keeps all logic pulses in step or

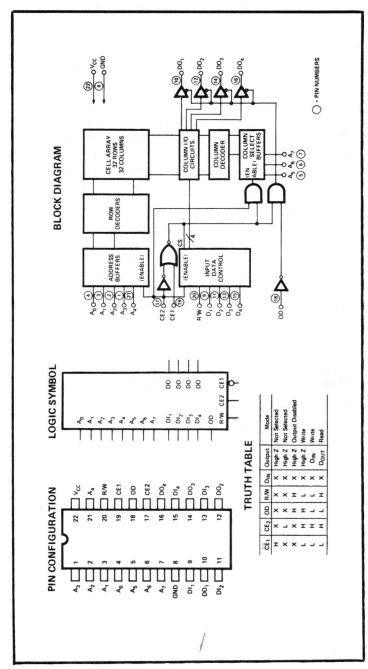

Fig. 3-14. INTEL's 5101 IC is a 256 × 4-bit static RAM (courtesy of INTEL).

Fig. 3-15. A pulse train generated by the clock.

synchronized. This is referred to as step-by-step or sequential logic systems. These sequential operations are controlled with a pulse signal from the clock. The clock device generates a precise pattern of 0's and 1's (pulse train), as illustrated in Fig. 3-15. The time of one complete clock cycle is called a period. The frequency of the clock is the reciprocal of the period. Astable multivibrators, such as the 555 IC timer shown in Fig. 3-16, operate at several megahertz are used to produce these clocking pulses. A crystal-controlled astable circuit is desired for microprocessor applications.

With the clocked-logic system, when an input condition changes, the output will not respond immediately, but waits until the arrival of the clock command. When this occurs, the output logic then responds. For this reason, then, clocked logic does not run wild, but steps through all program changes in an orderly manner. With logic step action counters, latches, shift registers, printers and various memory devices can now be utilized. Thus, every change occurs in steps with clocked logic which greatly reduces glitches and timing sequence mixups. The prime logic devices used with the clocked system are latches and various flip-flops.

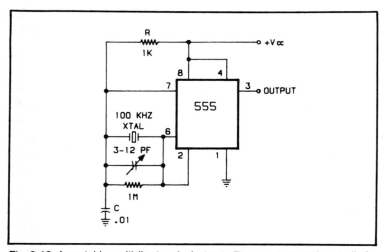

Fig. 3-16. An astable multivibrator clock circuit. This one is crystal controlled.

76

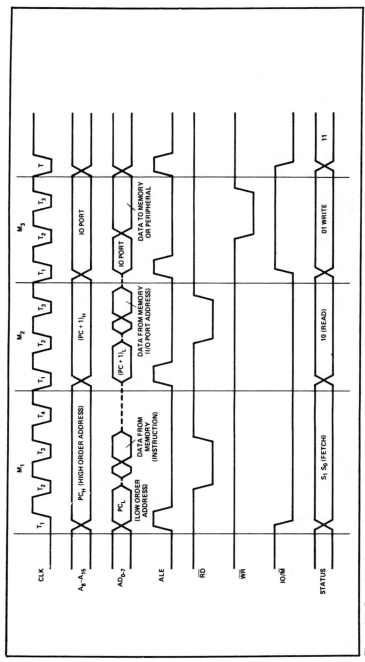

Fig. 3-17. Complex digital pulse waveforms for the INTEL 8085 microprocessor (courtesy of INTEL).

A bistable device is just another name for a flip-flop. This is a circuit in which the output has two stable states (output states 0 and 1) and can be caused to go into either of these states by an input signal. The circuit remains in that state permanently after the input signal is removed. Thus, a flip-flop is a device having two stable states with the capability of changing from one state to another with the application of a control signal, and remaining in that state after the signal has passed.

POSITIVE AND NEGATIVE EDGES

A digital scope waveform is a graphical representation of digital pulses that shows the variations in logic states as a function of time. This is usually referred to as the *systems timing diagram.*

The digital waveforms make it possible to show the logic conditions that exist at a certain point in time of a complex digital circuit. The digital circuit need not be complex, but the use of digital waveforms is essential for complex circuits. For simple logic circuits, the digital waveforms might need to show only one or two points in the logic circuit. For complex circuits, 10 or more digital waveforms may be needed to help you understand the various functions. An example of a complex train of pulses is shown in Fig. 3-17, this one for the basic timing of INTEL's 8085 microprocessor. For any digital waveform, the time progresses from left to right. The lower state, or baseline, of a digital waveform is usually considered to be the logic 0 state. The top portion of the pulse is the logic 1 state, or greater than +2.5 volts. You may assume that the change from a logic 0 state to a logic 1 state, which is called a positive edge, occurs almost instantaneously (in several nanoseconds or less). This change is represented by the vertical "step-up-line" in Fig. 3-18.

The old adage of "what goes up must come down" also applies to pulses. The drawing in Fig. 3-19 illustrates the change from a logic 1 to logic 0 by the vertical step-down line that is called the negative pulse edge.

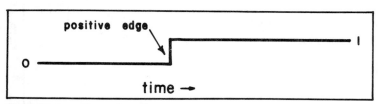

Fig. 3-18. A positive pulse edge.

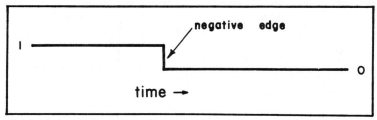

Fig. 3-19. A negative pulse edge.

RISE AND FALL TIME

It does appear—even on a fast scope—that the change occurs instantaneously, but it does not. With these state changes, there is both a rise time and a fall time.

The rise time is the time required for the positive leading edge of a pulse to rise from 10 percent to 90 percent of its final value. You will find that it is proportional to the time constant and is a measure of the steepness of the pulse wavefront. In digital electronics, rise time is the measured length of time required for an output voltage of a digital circuit to change from a low voltage level (logic 0) to a high voltage level (logic 1). The pulse rise-time phenomenon, shown in Fig. 3-20, should illustrate this to you more clearly.

Fall time is the time required for the trailing edge of a logic signal pulse to decrease from 90 percent to 10 percent of its initial value. In digital electronics, fall time is the measured length of time required for an output voltage of a digital circuit to change from a high voltage level (logic 1) to a low voltage level (logic 0).

Fig. 3-20. Pulse rise time.

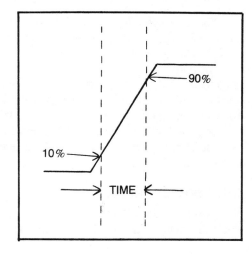

79

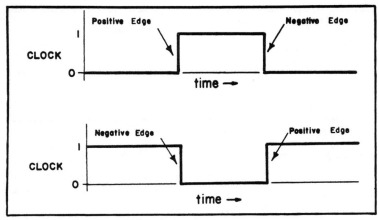

Fig. 3-21. Positive and negative clock pulse edges.

PROPAGATION DELAY

While thinking of rise and fall time, it would now be appropriate to discuss propagation delay as it pertains to pulse signal travel throughout digital/logic systems. Propagation delay is a measure of the time required for a logic pulse signal to travel through a logic device or series of logic devices forming a logic string. This delay also includes all of the interconnecting signal pulse lead paths between IC chips on the PC boards. It occurs as the result of four types of circuit delays: storage, rise, fall and turn-delay. This is the time between when the input signal crosses the threshold-voltage point and when the responding output voltage crosses the same voltage point.

The propagation time varies from different types of TTL gates. A low-power TTL gate chip has a propagation delay of as much as 33 ns, whereas a Schottky TTL chip has a propagation delay of only 3 ns. When you are working with very high digital frequencies and complex logic circuits, the concept of propagation delay can be quite important. Always keep this in mind, then, when troubleshooting these logic devices. Even when you may be breadboarding digital chips and testing them at low frequencies, the concept of propagation delay could be important and cannot be disregarded.

CLOCK AND TRIGGER PULSES

The 7490 decade counter is one type of many various digital electronic devices that contain flip-flops and change state upon the application of a clock pulse. When working with these flip-flops it is important to keep in mind which edge of a clock pulse the logic transition state occurs. Thus, whether it is a positive or negative edge transition must be considered when troubleshooting these devices. Figure 3-21 illustrates these positive- and negative-going clock pulses with the designated positive and negative pulse edges.

An edge-triggered flip-flop is one type of flip-flop in which some minimum clock signal rate of change, in volts/second, is a necessary condition for an output change to occur. And a trigger pulse is a pulse that starts the action in a flip-flop or other digital device. It may well be the positive or negative edges of the trigger pulses that start this action.

DIGITAL WAVEFORMS AND TIMING

A digital waveform is a graphical representation of a digital signal, showing the variations in logic state as a function of time. In a complex digital circuit, you need many different waveforms, corresponding to different points in the digital circuit, in order to understand the behavior of the circuit as a function of time.

To better understand this logic operation, we will start with the 7490 decade counter shown in Fig. 3-22. Note that the clock input is fed in at pin 14. A series of digital waveforms for the 7490 decade counter is shown in Fig. 3-23. The specific waveform points in the circuit and figure are as follows:

- The A clock input is at pin 14 of the 7490 chip.
- The A output is at pin 12 on the 7490 chip.
- The B output is at pin 9 on the 7490 chip.
- The C output is at pin 8 on the 7490 chip.
- The D output is at pin 11 on the 7490 chip.

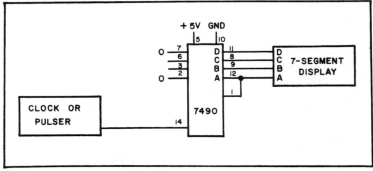

Fig. 3-22. Block diagram of the 7490 decade counter.

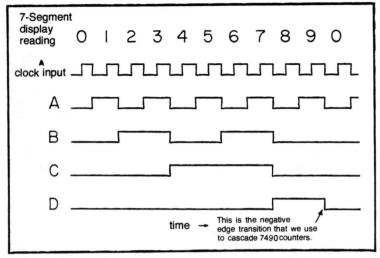

Fig. 3-23. Series of digital waveforms for the 7490 decade counter.

Let's now consider the transition from 3 to 4 on the seven-segment display. When the display is at 3, the four outputs of the 7490 counter have the following logic states:

$$A = 1$$
$$B = 1$$
$$C = 0$$
$$D = 0$$

These logic states correspond to the 4-bit binary-coded decimal (BCD) word 0011, which corresponds to 3 on the display. Now observe what happens on the negative edge of the clock pulse between 3 and 4. We see that both A and B return to logic 0 and C goes to logic 1. The new BCD output from the counter is 0100, which corresponds to 4 on the display.

Another important transition is from 9 to 0 on the seven-segment display. This transition occurs at the negative edge of the single clock pulse at output D. For every 10 full clock pulses input at the A clock input pin, there is a single output clock pulse at output D. This is the reason for calling the 7490 decade counter a divide-by-ten counter.

THE 7490 DECADE COUNTERS

To *cascade* means to arrange two or more similar digital circuits or integrated circuit chips in a way that the output of one circuit

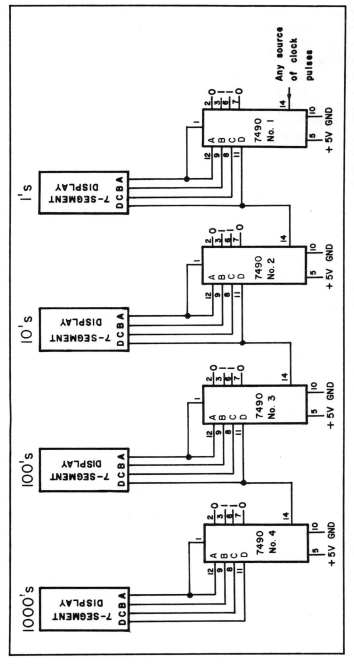

Fig. 3-24. Four cascaded 7490 decade counters, each of which is connected to its own seven-segment LED display. This circuit can count from 0000 to 9999.

83

or chip provides the input of the next one. This cascading process can continue for as many decades as required. Note the four cascaded decade counters shown in Fig. 3-24. The diagram is arranged so that the most significant digit—the 1000's digit—is on the far left, and the least significant digit, the 1's digit is on the far right. Such a circuit permits you to count clock pulses from 0000 to 9999. Tapping off the four D outputs from the counters will provide divide-by-ten, divide-by-hundred, divide-by-thousand and divide-by-ten thousand outputs.

Chapter 4
Using The Oscilloscope
for Digital Troubleshooting

A very obvious and yet most useful feature of two or more trace oscilloscope is they have the capability for viewing two or more waveforms simultaneously that are frequency or phase related, or that have a common synchronizing voltage, such as in digital/logic circuitry. Simultaneous viewing of cause-and-effect waveforms is an invaluable aid to the circuit designer or technician.

FREQUENCY DIVIDER WAVEFORMS

The waveform illustrated in Fig. 4-1 is found in a basic divide-by-two circuit. The channel A waveform is the clock pulse train reference. References B and C indicate the possible outputs of the divide-by-two circuitry. Also indicated in Fig. 4-1 are the settings of specific oscilloscope controls for viewing these waveforms. In addition to these basic control settings, the TRIGGER LEVEL control, as well as the channel A and channel B VERTICAL POSITION controls should be set as required to produce viewable patterns. Figure 4-1 indicates waveform levels of 2 cm. If the exact voltage amplitude of the channel A and B waveforms are desired, the channel A and B VARIABLE controls must be placed in the CAL position. The control adjustments are for a B&K model 1471B dual-trace scope, such as the one shown in Fig. 4-2. The channel B waveform may be either of the ones indicated in B or C. In C, the divide-by-two output waveform is shown for the case where the output circuitry responds to a negative-going waveform. In this

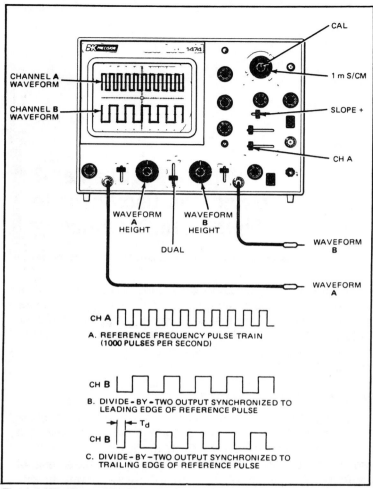

Fig. 4-1. Waveforms found in a divide-by-two circuit.

case, the output waveform is shifted with respect to the leading edge of the reference pulse by a time interval corresponding to the pulse width.

DIVIDE-BY-EIGHT CIRCUIT WAVEFORM

The waveform of Fig. 4-3 indicates the relationship for a basic divide-by-eight circuit. You need only to use the basic oscilloscope settings to view these waveforms. The reference frequency of Fig. 4-3A is fed to the channel A input, and the divide-by-eight output is

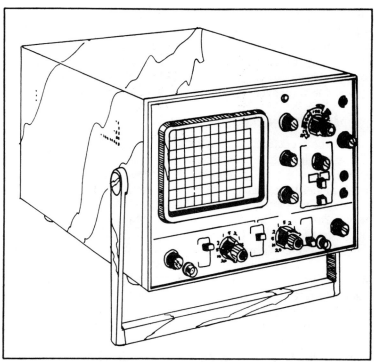

Fig. 4-2. B & K model 1471 B dual-trace oscilloscope.

fed to the channel B input. The B waveform reference indicates the ideal time relationship between the input pulse and the output pulse.

In an application where the logic circuitry is operating at or near its maximum design frequency, the accumulated rise time effects of

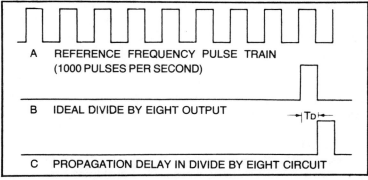

Fig. 4-3. Waveforms found in a divide-by-eight circuit.

87

the consecutive stages produce a built-in time propagation delay which can be significant in a critical circuit and must be compensated for. Figure 4-3 indicates the possible time delay that can be introduced into a frequency divider circuit. By using a dual-trace oscilloscope, the input and output waveforms can be superimposed to determine the exact amount of propagation delay that occurs.

PROPAGATION TIME MEASUREMENT

In the preceding paragraph we looked at propagation delay in a divide-by-eight circuit. Significant propagation delay may occur in any circuit with several consecutive stages. A scope, such as the B&K model 1474, has features which allow for simplified measurements of propagation delay. Figure 4-4 shows the resultant ‘waveforms when the dual-trace presentation is combined into a single-trace presentation by selecting the ADD position of the MODE switch. With the channel B polarity switch in the NORM position, the two inputs are algebraically added in a single-trace display. Similarly, in the invert position the two inputs are algebraically subtracted. Either position provides a precise display of the propagation time (T_p). By using the calibrated time measurement, propagation time can be calculated. A more precise measurement can be obtained if the T_p portion of the waveform is expanded horizontally. Use the HORIZONTAL SWEEP (5×) EXPANSION control for this purpose. It might also be possible to view the desired portion of the waveform at a faster time base speed.

DIGITAL CIRCUIT TIME RELATIONSHIP

A dual-trace oscilloscope is a necessity in designing, building and troubleshooting digital equipment. A dual-trace scope permits easy comparison of time relationships between two waveforms.

In digital devices it is common for a large number of circuits to be synchronized, or to have a specific time relationship to each other. Many of the circuits are frequency dividers that have just been described, but many waveforms are often time-related in many other combinations. In the dynamic state, some of the waveforms change, depending upon the input or mode of operation. Figure 4-5 shows a typical digital circuit and identifies several of the points at which waveform measurements are appropriate. Figure 4-6 shows the normal waveforms to be expected at each of these points. Their timing relationships to one or more of the other waveforms are known to be correct. The dual-trace oscilloscope allows this comparison to be made. For scoping this system,

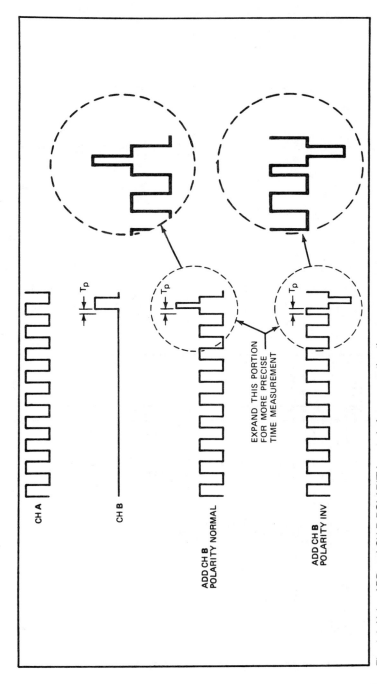

Fig. 4-4. Using ADD and CH B POLARITY controls for propagation time measurement.

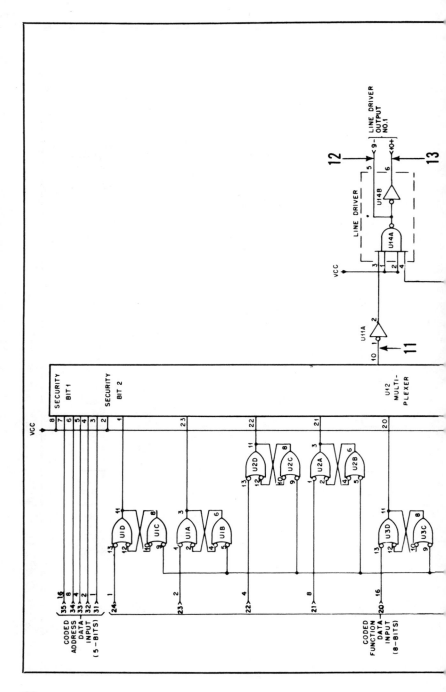

90

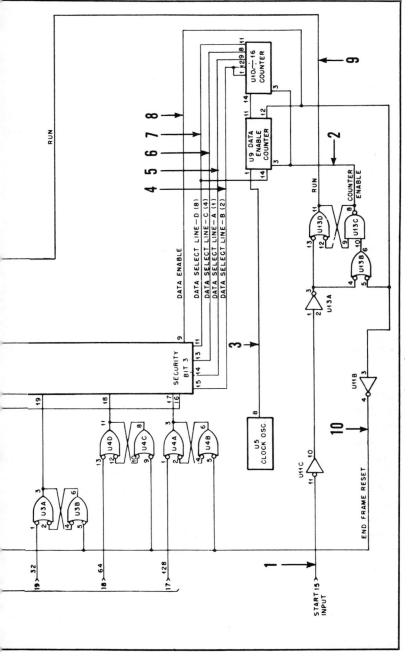

Fig. 4-5. Typical digital circuit using several time-related waveforms.

91

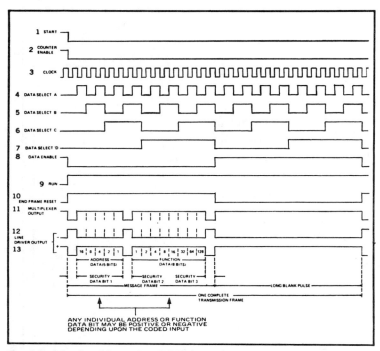

Fig. 4-6. A family of time-related digital waveforms.

waveform 3 would be displayed on channel A and waveforms 4 through 8, and 10, would be successively displayed on channel B, although other timing comparisons might be desired. Waveforms 11 through 13 would probably be viewed on channel B, and waveforms 8 or 4 would be viewed on channel A of the oscilloscope.

In the family of time-related waveforms shown in Fig. 4-6, waveform 8 or 10 may be used as the sync source for viewing all of the waveforms, because there is only one triggering pulse per frame. You can also switch the scope to external sync by using waveform 8 or 10 as the sync source. With external sync, any of the waveforms are viewable without readjustment of the sync controls. Waveforms 4 through 7 should not be used as the sync source because they do not contain a triggering pulse at the start of the frame. In most cases, it would not be necessary to view the entire waveforms as shown in Fig. 4-6. In fact, there are many times when a clear examination of a portion of the waveforms is appropriate. In such cases, it is recommended that the sync remain unchanged while time-base speed or ×5 magnification be used to expand the pulse waveform display. A four-channel scope, such as the Philips PM 3214 shown in Fig. 4-7, will let you view a family of time-related waveforms found in microprocessor circuits more accurately and easily.

CLOCK OR PULSE GENERATION

Microprocessor systems and most all digital/logic devices require some type of clock pulse in order to perform and time the various functions. The clock generates accurately timed pulses and may be crystal controlled. The logic systems are gated or enabled by these clock pulses. The faster the clock frequency, the more functions that can be performed, but this speed is limited by response time of the ICs used in the system. Clocks vary from simple local devices to the very diverse and complex systems.

The simple clock puts out equally spaced pulses and should be as narrow as possible and still enable the gates. The reason for the narrow clock pulses is to discriminate against noise pulses or glitches. Some systems require a two-phase clock, such as the 8080A microprocessor IC that we will look at shortly.

Thus, the clock is the very heart of most digital/logic systems. For this reason then, the clock pulses should be one of the first items to be checked with the scope when troubleshooting these systems.

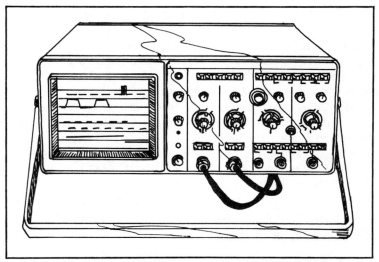

Fig. 4-7. Philips model 3214 four-channel oscilloscope used for digital troubleshooting.

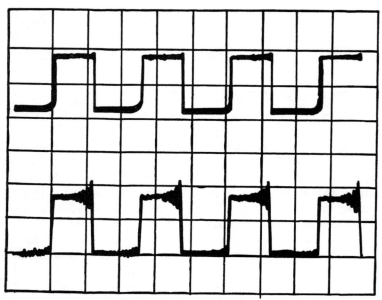

Fig. 4-8. Pulse distortion when the probe shield is not grounded.

One note of caution when using a scope probe for observing these clock pulses. If the shielded probe case of the oscilloscope is not properly grounded, erroneous clock pulse waveforms on the scope might trick you into seeing a distorted pulse when there is none. Not only should the ground lead from the scope case be connected to the chassis ground of the equipment under test, but the ground shield of the probe must be connected to the ground pin of the clock IC you are testing. This caution is readily illustrated for a clock pulse shown in the bottom trace of Fig. 4-8 where the probe shield was not grounded. Note the ringing distortion on the pulse waveforms. A clean clock pulse is shown in the top trace of the figure with the probe shield properly grounded. Always use an ×10 attenuation scope probe for checking clock and logic pulses. These clock pulses can radiate, or transmit, very potent radio frequency signals (if the complete unit is not properly shielded and I/O lines filtered) and can cause interference in other nearby electronic devices. Thus, if you have some strange acting equipment problems, be on the alert for this type of rf spectrum pollution.

Clock Inputs for the 8080A

An 8080A microprocessor chip requires a two-phase clock pulse input. A *clock* in digital/logic jargon is a device that

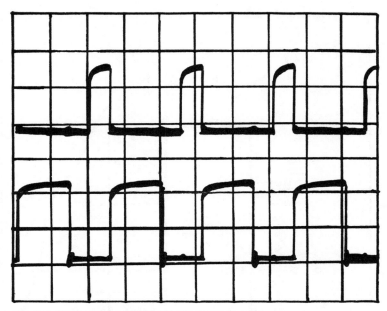

Fig. 4-9. Timing of the 8080A two-phase clock pulses.

generates at least one clock pulse, or a timing device that provides a continuous series of timing pulses. A two-phase clock is a two-input timing device that provides two continuous series of timing pulses that are synchronized together with a single clock pulse from the second series always following a single clock pulse from the first series. Figure 4-9 shows the timing of these two clock pulses. The top trace is the phase 1, and the bottom trace is the phase 2 clock pulse.

Fig. 4-10. 8080A pinout diagram.

```
A₁₀  O——  1         40  ——O  A₁₁
GND  O——  2         39  ——O  A₁₄
 D₄  O——  3         38  ——O  A₁₃
 D₅  O——  4         37  ——O  A₁₂
 D₆  O——  5         36  ——O  A₁₅
 D₇  O——  6         35  ——O  A₉
 D₃  O——  7         34  ——O  A₈
 D₂  O——  8   INTEL 33  ——O  A₇
 D₁  O——  9         32  ——O  A₆
 D₀  O——  10  8080  31  ——O  A₅
-5V  O——  11        30  ——O  A₄
RESET O—— 12        29  ——O  A₃
HOLD O——  13        28  O—  +12V
 INT O——  14        27  ——O  A₂
  ?  O——  15        26  ——O  A₁
INTE O——  16        25  ——O  A₀
DBIN O——  17        24  ——O  WAIT
 WR̄  O——  18        23  O—  READY
SYNC O——  19        22  O—  ϕ₁
+5V  O——  20        21  ——O  HLDA
```

95

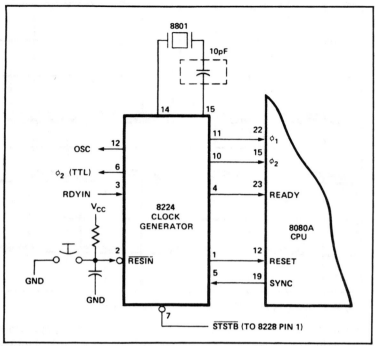

Fig. 4-11. 8224 clock block diagram.

It is stated in the 8080A specifications that the minimum pulse width for clock phase 1 is 60 ns, and the phase 2 clock pulse width is 220 ns. Refer to Fig. 4-10 for the pinouts of the INTEL 8080A chip. This is a two-phase nonoverlapping clock system. These clock pulses can be generated with an INTEL 8224 clock generator chip.

Clock Frequency Check with a Counter

A frequency counter is now an essential instrument for checking out digital/logic, microprocessor, PLL and other divider systems now found in almost all electronic devices encountered by the electronics service technician. Your first step for isolating problems in a nonoperational logic system is to check for clock operation and correct clock frequency. The frequency counter is used to check the output from the clock generator chip. If you were troubleshooting a system that uses the popular 8080A microprocessor, these two check points would be pins 10 and 11 of the 8224 clock generator chip shown in pinout and block diagram of Fig. 4-11. The 8080A requires two phase clock signals at pins 15 and 22. This clock

96

generator IC also requires a crystal for accurate frequency generation and control.

Loop Pickup Counter Measurements

There may be cases where you cannot make direct connections to the clock input signal or do not want to because of circuit loading. The probe capacitance of the frequency counter could cause the frequency of the oscillator to change, or stop the clock oscillator from running in a worst-case condition. The pickup loop (shown near the clock crystal in Fig. 4-12) allows signals to be picked up without a direct probe connection. For this application, the inductive loop is used to pick off the frequency pulses quickly, without any direct connections. This action eliminates any interference with the measured circuit. You may not obtain an accurate count of the clock pulses because the input signal to the frequency counter from the pickup loop will be a sawtooth or sinewave shape because of coil induction. The pickup loop can also be connected to the input of the scope to take a quick look at various oscillator signals.

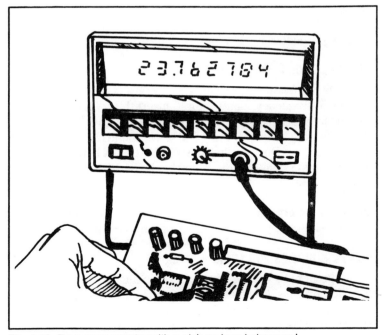

Fig. 4-12. Frequency counter with a pick-up loop being used.

Inductive Pickup Loop Applications

For these tests we are using the Sencore model FC51 1-GHz frequency counter and rf pickup loop. Select the desired input, read rate and frequency range. Place the pickup loop near a capacitor or coil in the oscillator circuit to be tested. If an unstable count is obtained, reposition the pickup loop in order to stabilize the count. If no count is obtained, turn over the pickup loop (which reverses the polarity of the pickup loops coil), or select a different component in the circuit.

The pick-up loop will work best when placed next to or around a coil. However, a high-sensitivity counter will let you pickup signals from capacitors, transistors, ICs or crystals in most circuits.

Most clocks in digital/logic systems use a clock to keep the frequency pulses stable and accurate. Should the clock not operate or be off frequency, the crystal would be the prime component suspect. To check this crystal is an easy task to perform if you have a Sencore FC51 frequency counter. The crystal check feature on this instrument allows any crystal with a fundamental frequency of 1 to 20 MHz to be checked. Note in Fig. 4-13 that a crystal is inserted in the front panel universal crystal socket to check for crystal activity. The crystal will be made to resonate at its fundamental operating frequency.

CRYSTAL CHECK PROCEDURE

Use the following procedure to check a crystal with the Sencore FC51 frequency counter. First, insert the crystal to be tested into the front panel crystal check socket. Select the desired READ RATE button. Depress the 20-kHz to 100-kHz FREQUENCY RANGE button. Depress the CRYSTAL CHECK button. Read the fundamental crystal frequency on the digital LED readout of the counter.

The crystal check reads the approximate fundamental frequency of the crystal under test. Defective or inoperative crystals will be indicated by an intermittent or zero counter readout.

POWER SUPPLIES FOR LOGIC SYSTEMS

A proper DC voltage power source is required for operation of the microprocessor and logic systems that have been discussed in this book. In fact, all digital/logic systems must have very precise regulated DC power supplies that are well filtered. Use your scope to check for a smooth DC output voltage from the power supply and

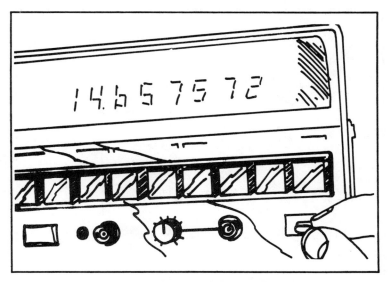

Fig. 4-13. Crystal check on a Sencore FC51 frequency counter.

check for correct regulated DC voltage levels to all logic circuits with a DVM. Most of these voltage supplies are electronically regulated and filtered.

The scope can be used to monitor the DC supply lines in order to catch spikes in TTL (transistor-transistor logic) systems as the gates function and filters or bypass capacitors may have opened up. Thus, a very fast, wide-band triggered-sweep scope is required to detect these transient pulses.

When a TTL circuit is switched from a low to a high state, transients occur on the supply voltage line because of the TTL totem pole output action. Note the typical TTL gate circuit shown in Fig. 4-14. When the logic level goes high, it is actually short circuiting the supply voltage during a brief period.

If several gates switch on simultaneously, the current spike on the supply line is increased linearly with the number of gates. These spikes or glitches, which are caused by insufficient DC supply line filtering, can trigger on fast TTL gates and be quite fatal. By *fatal* we mean to destroy information stored in memory systems (PROMs, ROMs, RAMs, etc.). So use your scope to check those DC voltage power-supply lines for open filter or bypass capacitors.

To track down these spikes or glitches in a microprocessor system, you not only need to check at the DC power-supply voltage

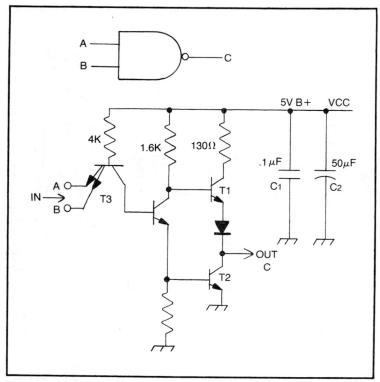

Fig. 4-14. Typical TTL gate circuit.

output terminals, but at various filter or bypass points throughout the system. You will notice that there are many filter and bypass capacitors located throughout any logic device that contains many gates. The logic pulse scope trace shown in Fig. 4-15 is of a properly operating gate. Should a filter capacitor become open in this stage, a scope pulse like that shown in Fig. 4-16 may well develop. Note the small spikes as the pulse goes from a high to a low transition. The amplitude of these spikes will vary as to which filter capacitor C1 or C2, is faulty, in the case of the TTL gate circuit shown in Fig. 4-14.

If you use the scope to check the DC-regulated voltage coming out of the logic system power supply, you should see a smooth, clean trace, such as shown in the top trace of Fig. 4-17. This is true even with a very high vertical scope AMPLIFIER GAIN setting. Should trouble occur in the electronically regulated DC circuit or filter capacitors, some hash or pulses that are shown in the bottom scope trace of Fig. 4-17 will show up.

100

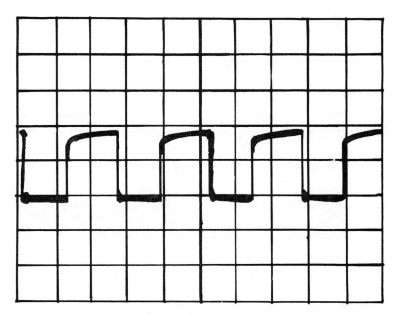

Fig. 4-15. Pulse of a properly operating gate.

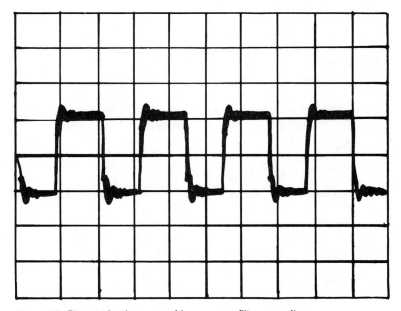

Fig. 4-16. Distorted pulse caused by an open filter capacitor.

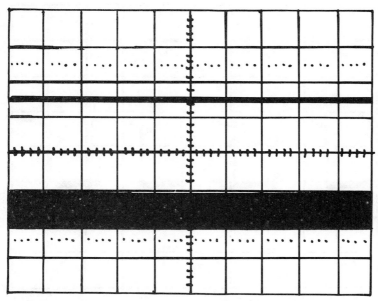

Fig. 4-17. The top trace indicates proper filtering, and the bottom trace hash shows a poor filtering system.

MICROCOMPUTER POWER SUPPLY

A well regulated power supply for a microcomputer system is shown in the block diagram of Fig. 4-18. Note that it produces a regulated +5 volts at 3 amps and a +12 volts and −12 volts at .5 amp which supplies all computer operations. This power supply is found in the Processor Technology model SOL-20 minicomputer system. To accurately measure these critical DC voltages that must be supplied to logic devices, a digital voltmeter is an ideal instrument for troubleshooting logic circuits of all types.

LAB SCIENCE VLA-1000 LOGIC ANALYZER

The Lab Science VLA-1000 shown in Fig. 4-19 is a general-purpose logic analyzer designed for logic designers and troubleshooters. The VLA-1000 probes, selects and records up to 16 parallel digital inputs simultaneously. It stores and arranges this data in one of four possible output formats, and then displays this data on an ordinary X-Y oscilloscope.

The VLA-1000 analyzer has been specifically designed to operate with most scopes that have a horizontal input. Even AC-coupled scopes, if their bandwidth is at least from 10 Hz to 100 kHz,

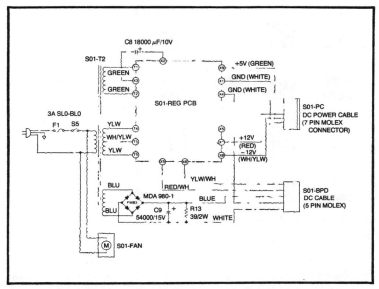

Fig. 4-18. Block diagram of the SOL-20 power supply.

will present an excellent display in all modes. The oscilloscope should be capable of full-screen deflection for ±2 volts DC input to both horizontal and vertical amplifiers, and should have input impedances of 100K ohm or greater. Even the lowest price, general-purpose scopes can meet these specs. The dual-trace D/A output mode requires a dual-trace scope, but you can observe each byte separately on a single-trace scope and obtain the same information.

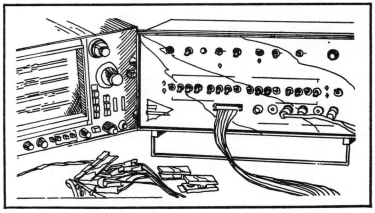

Fig. 4-19. Lab Science VLA-1000 setup.

103

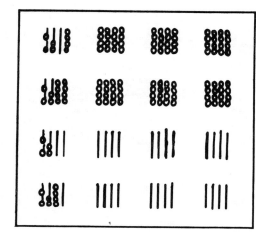

Fig. 4-20. DATA domain.

Procedure and Operation

To prepare the VLA-1000 logic analyzer for operation, connect the VLA-1000 to the oscilloscope and set up the VLA-1000 front panel switches as follows:

- Set all PATTERN RECOGNITION WORD switches to X.
- Set DELAY: EVENTS/CLOCKS to CLOCKS.
- Set NORM/DELAY/LOAD DELAY to NORM.
- Set REPETITIVE/SINGLE to SINGLE.
- Set POS/MID/NEG to POS.
- Set DATA DOMAIN/WAVESHAPE/MAP MODE to DATA DOMAIN.

Switch the ON/POWER AC line switch to ON. Now you should see presented on the scope 256 1's and 0's, as in Fig. 4-20. Adjust the intensity, focus, vertical and horizontal gain and positioning of the scope to give a viewable display. To check WAVESHAPE mode, set the DATA DOMAIN/WAVESHAPE/MAP MODE switch to WAVESHAPE. This should give a display similar to that in Fig. 4-21. To check MAP MODE, set the DATA DOMAIN/WAVESHAPE/MAP MODE switch to MAP MODE. This display will probably not look like the MAP MODE shown in Fig. 4-22, but will most likely be just a few dots near either the upper left or upper right of the scope screen (location 0000 16). This is because the VLA-1000 memory has come up loaded with mostly zeros. If the cluster of dots is in the upper left corner, change to the opposite polarity HORIZ + jack on the VLA-1000 panel, and use only that polarity for this scope.

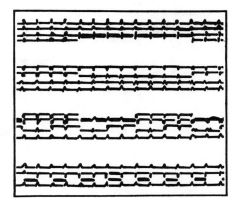

Fig. 4-21. Waveshape mode.

To check the DUAL-TRACE D/A mode, set up the scope for externally triggered horizontal sweep operation. Now set the horizontal sweep speed to 1 ms/division, connect the VLA-1000 DISPLAY SYNC output jack to the external trigger input of the oscilloscope, and connect the selected (from the previous step) + HORIZ output jack to the second vertical input channel of the scope. Set both VERTICAL CHANNEL SENSITIVITIES to 2 V/division. This display will probably not look much like the one shown in Fig. 4-23, because the memory is loaded with mostly zeros. It does, however, represent the same data as the other three display modes.

To illustrate a more common use of the EVENTS DELAY capability, set the REPETITIVE/SINGLE switch to SINGLE. Disconnect the clock from the test circuit so it will stop counting. Next, momentarily depress the RESET switch to the VLA-1000. Recon-

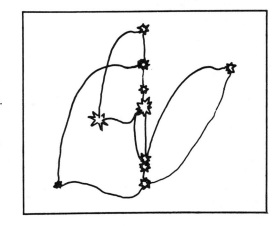

Fig. 4-22. Map mode.

105

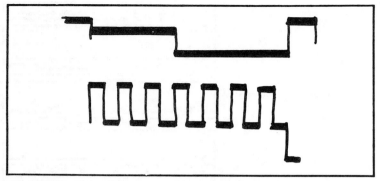

Fig. 4-23. Dual-trace D/A upper and lower bytes.

nect the clock to the test circuit allowing it to resume counting. The VLA-1000 will pass over the first three occurences of the all-zero pattern recognition word and then record and display the data desired indefinitely until restarted by either depressing the RESET switch or switching the REPETITIVE/SINGLE switch back to REPETITIVE. This feature allows the logic designer or troubleshooter to examine data at practically any time slot window of its sequential states. The VLA-1000 has no provision for delaying on both clocks and events in the same operation, but the POS/MID/NEG control does provide the user the capability to observe data 15 clocks either before or after the desired delay number of events.

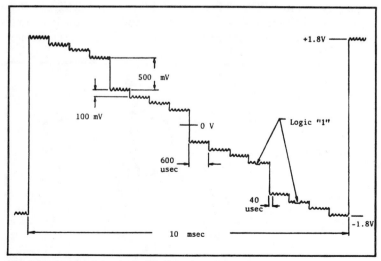

Fig. 4-24. Horizontal output with data domain.

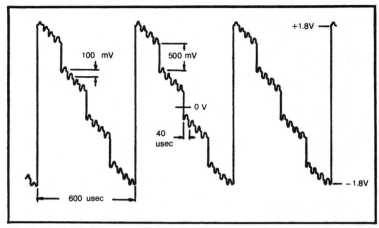

Fig. 4-25. Vertical output with data domain.

Output Waveforms

Figures 4-24 through 4-27 show the waveforms of the VLA-1000 for the VERT and HORIZ outputs indicated, in data domain and waveshape modes, with voltage levels and timing indicated. For individual units, these may vary ±20 percent from those shown.

Theory of Operation

The VLA-1000 block diagram, shown in Fig. 4-28, illustrates the functional groups of the instrument.·For clarity, all details have not been shown.

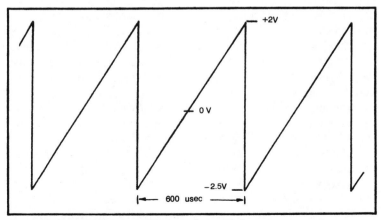

Fig. 4-26. Horizontal output with waveshape mode.

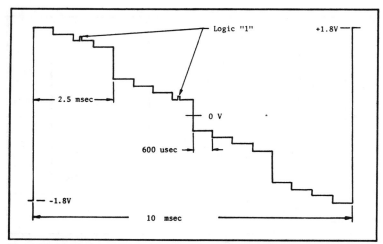

Fig. 4-27. Vertical output with waveshape mode.

Theory of Operation

The purpose of a logic analyzer is to selectively record and display data from a complex digital electronic circuit and present it on the screen of an oscilloscope in an easily recognizable format. The VLA-1000 accomplishes this task by recording 16 data inputs, strobed by an externally supplied synchronous clock, until a selected pattern recognition word is recognized, and then presenting this digital word along with 15 adjacent words in one of four possible display formats: data domain, waveshape, map mode, or dual trace D/A. At the upper left of the block diagram, 16 data lines enter the instrument, are buffered, inverted and conditioned to TTL levels and then clocked into a 16-bit, 1-word storage register to produce 32 terms for input to the PATTERN RECOGNITION switches as well as to the 16-bit × 16-word static RAM memory. The address lines of this memory are driven by a four-stage real word binary counter. An identical four-stage pseudoword binary counter shares a common clock but is preset by the timing and control logic to accommodate the POS/MID/NEG display arrangement selected by the user. This operation can be seen in the VLA-1000 control logic flow chart shown in Fig. 4-29.

The carry bit from the pseudoword counter clocks a four-stage bit counter, which drives the address lines of a one-of-six data selector, which produces the 256 bits of stored memory serially, one bit per 40 U sec. This serial data bit line drives an analog gate to produce 1's and 0's as required in the data domain mode, and the

LSB of a vertical D/A converter in waveshape mode. Two 8-bit data selectors steer data and position information into the two D/A converters (vertical and horizontal) to present data, as required, for the selected output mode. A ramp generator provides horizontal sweeps for waveshape mode, and a quadrature oscillator provides sine and cosine waveforms for data domain mode. The D/A converters are driven directly by the memory MS byte and LS byte, respectively, in map mode and dual-trace D/A mode.

A 16-bit DELAY COUNT STORAGE REGISTER is loaded by depressing the LOAD switch on the panel. This stored word controls the count down of the 16-bit bcd counter for events or clocks delay (up to 9999) from the selected pattern recognition word.

MICROPROCESSOR APPLICATIONS

In the following diagrams, Figs. 4-30 through 4-33, you will find timing and CPU pinout data and *selective store* clock-qualifying information for some microprocessors in use today. This information is intended as only a guide to the user and should be used as such. Most microprocessors have different timing characteristics depending upon the instruction being executed: fetch, execute, I/O, DMA, etc. Therefore, the timing diagram and clock-qualifiying circuit shown might not display the desired address bus or data information. In general, address information is available during longer portions of an instruction cycle than is valid data. For this reason, it is best to first locate the sequential address information "window" desired, and then refine the choice of a data clock to present the controlling address bits, substituting data bus inputs for the unchanging or "don't care" address bits, up to the maximum capacity of 16 input data lines of the VLA-1000.

Another point to remember is that tri-stated or floated inputs can only be represented in the display as 1's or 0's (usually 1's). This display can sometimes be confusing, especially when the user insists on explaining every bit in a truth table or map mode display. Also, although the CPU pinout is given for each microprocessor, it is far better to trace each signal through the circuit to find a buffered equivalent signal, in order to improve noise immunity and isolation from the processor. Another caution: Many second-source suppliers do not use the exact timing relationships that the particular, original manufacturer does. For this reason, it is best to use the specific CPU manufacturer's data sheets.

The selective store clock-qualification schematics shown for some of the microprocessors provide a means to observe only

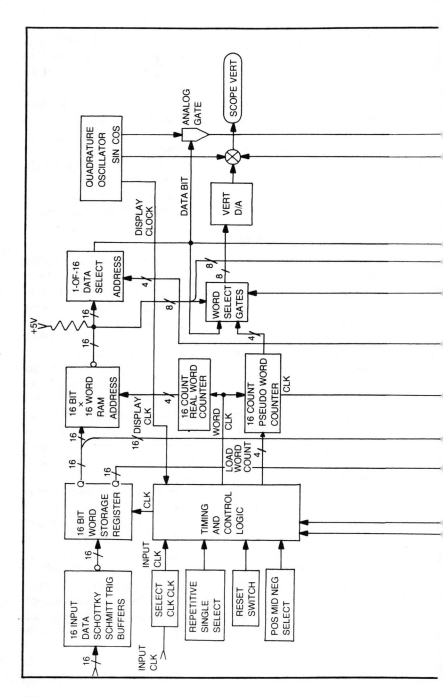

110

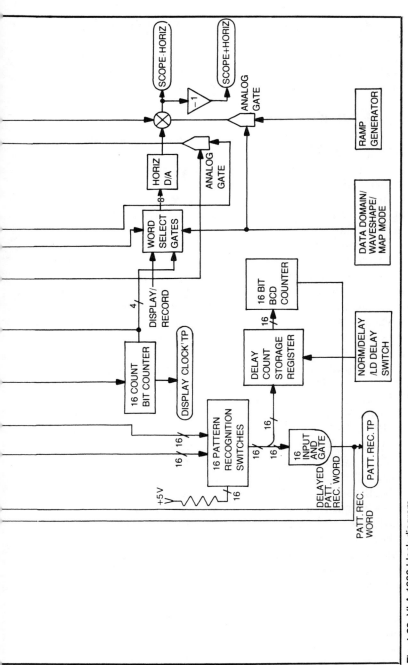

Fig. 4-28. VLA-1000 block diagram.

111

qualified data. This is necessary when address and data buses are time-multiplexed to provide clocking-in of only valid data. Continuous use of the VLA-1000 tied to a microprocessor development system should yield a much broader understanding of the detailed system operation and an insight into design optimization.

SPIKE OR GLITCH LOCATOR

Here is a trick with the triggered-sweep scope that may help you locate an intermittent spike or pulse that at times may be found riding on the regulated DC voltage supplies in digital/logic systems. For this testing technique, you will need a scope that has a single-sweep mode or a one-shot sweep mode. This feature will usually be found on a scope with a delaying time base or an A-delayed-by-B-time base generator.

The reason for using this technique is that these spikes are very narrow—usually only 10 or 20 ns long—which makes them difficult to see even on a wide-band (30- to 50-MHz) scope. Also, they are usually random in nature. With this setup, you can use the ready light, which shows the one-shot has been armed, for indicating when a spike has occurred, even if you are not looking at the scope screen. Thus, the scope becomes an automatic glitch monitor.

Set up the scope as follows to catch or see an intermittent spike that may occur on the regulated DC voltage power-supply lines. Obviously, this technique cannot be used on circuit lines that normally carry pulse signals. To activate the one-shot mode, depress the SINGLE SWEEP button as shown in Fig. 4-34. When a spike is detected in the vertical amplifier, the sweep will be triggered on for one single trace, and the ready light will go off. Punch the SINGLE SWEEP button again and the ready light will come back on, indicating that the sweep has been armed again. What we are doing is using the ready light as a visual monitor indicator to determine when a spike has occurred in the circuit under test. Consequently, you do not have to watch constantly the scope screen and can do other service work on the bench. Also, although the spike may be so narrow that you cannot see it on the scope, there be an indication of some action when the single-sweep mode has been fired.

You may have to try various time base generator settings—negative or positive slope (sync) and vertical amplifier gain levels—in order to obtain the spike that will trigger on the single-sweep trace. Some scopes will have a TRIGGER LEVEL control that may need to be varied. The CRT INTENSITY control level should also

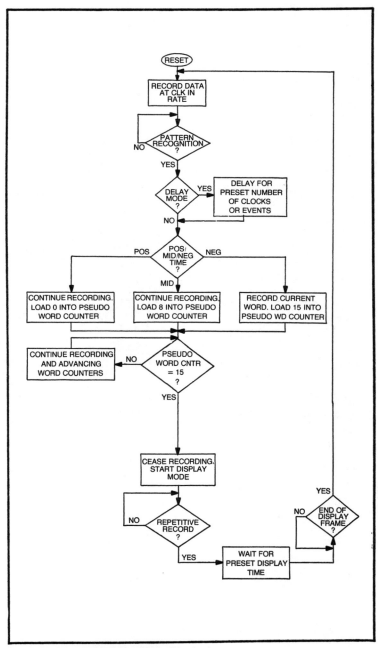

Fig. 4-29. VLA-1000 control logic flowchart.

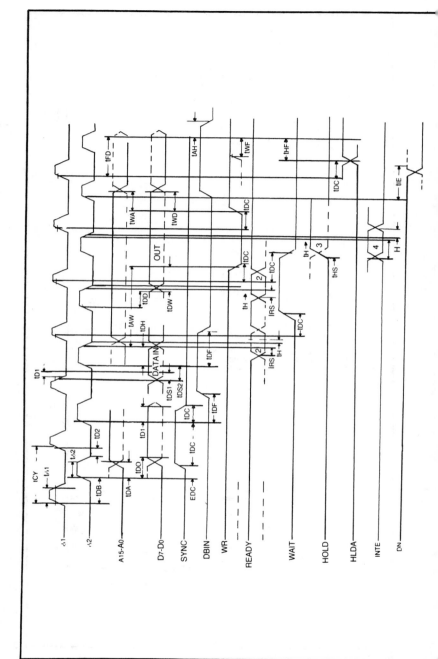

114

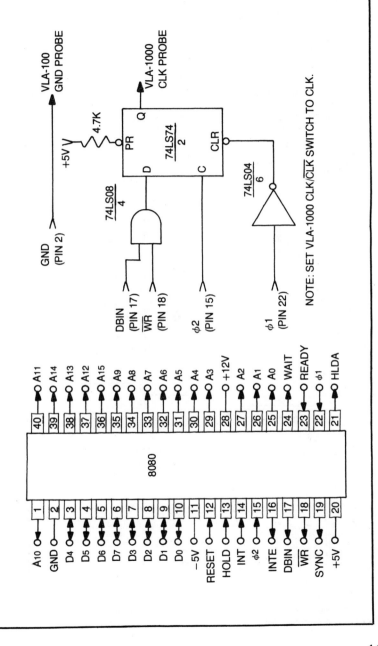

Fig. 4-30. The INTEL 8080A microprocessor (courtesy of INTEL).

115

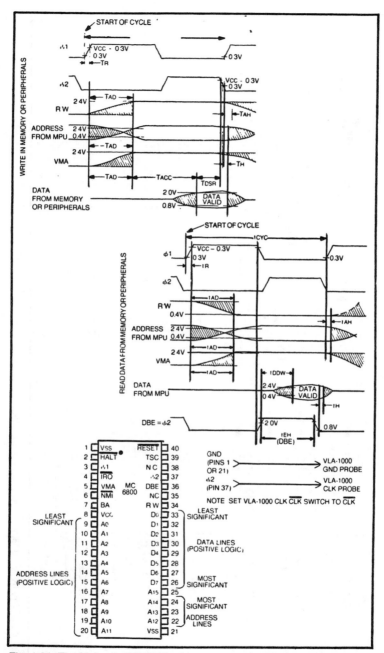

Fig. 4-31. The Motorola MC 6800 microprocessor (courtesy of Motorola).

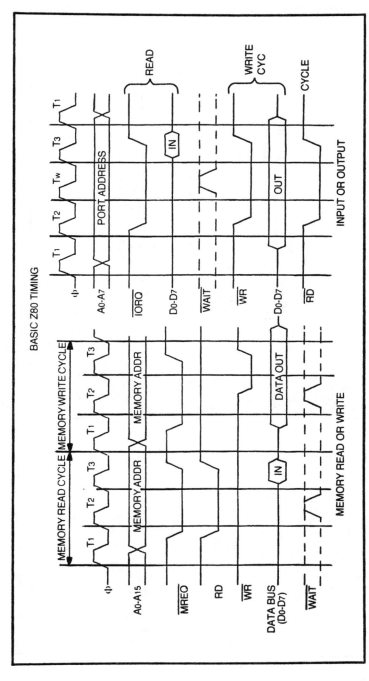

Fig. 4-32. The ZIGLO Z-80 microprocessor.

117

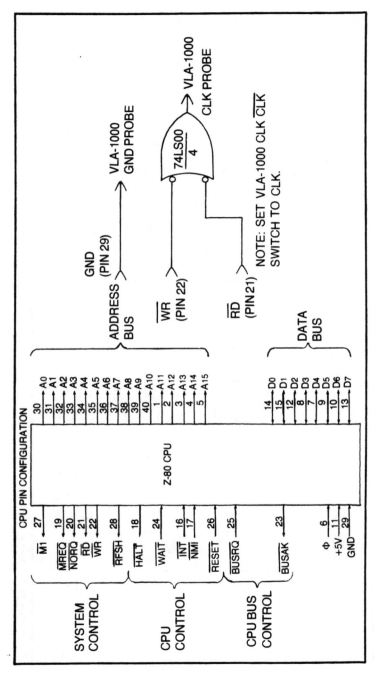

Fig. 4-32. The ZIGLO Z-80 microprocessor (continued from page 117).

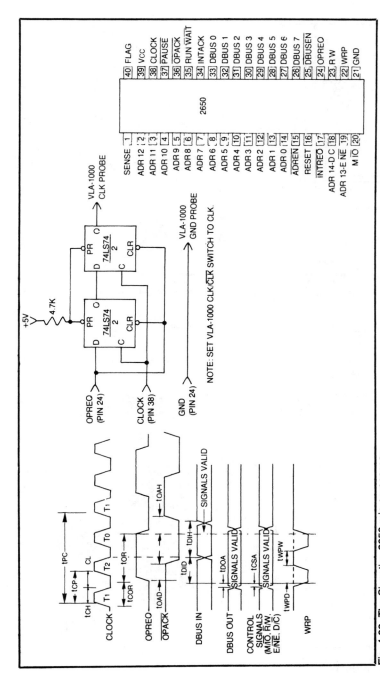

Fig. 4-33. The Signetics 2650 microprocessor.

119

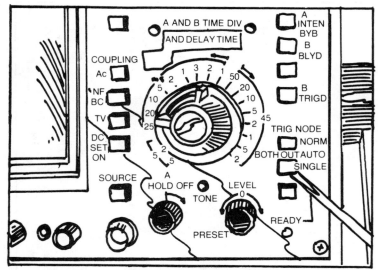

Fig. 4-34. Oscilloscope panel showing locations of the SINGLE-SWEEP button and ready light.

be adjusted for a bright trace, because there will only be one sweep across the screen. Thus, the one shot sweep enables you to know a spike has occurred that you might not normally be able to see on the scope trace.

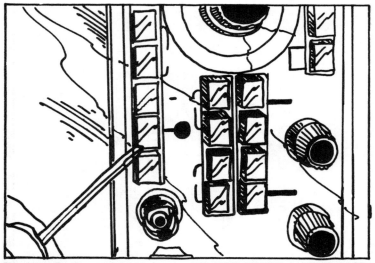

Fig. 4-35. Oscilloscope panel showing DELAYED-SWEEP and TIME BASE GENERATOR controls.

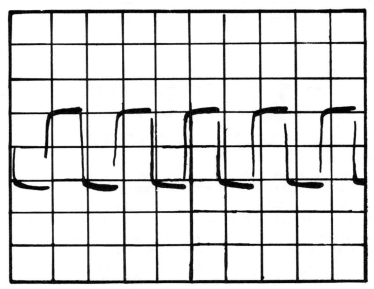

Fig. 4-36. Pulses seen with normal scope operation.

DELAYED-SWEEP SCOPE TRACE

Most triggered-sweep oscilloscopes that have a single-sweep feature (one shot) also have delayed-sweep functions. The controls, shown in Fig. 4-35, include A and B TIME BASE GENERATOR, A MAIN SWEEP, A-INTENSIFIED-BY-B, B DELAYED-SWEEP and DELAY TIME controls. The A and B delayed-sweep modes can be used to look at digital logic pulses and any other complex waveforms that you must observe in greater detail. This delayed sweep will stretch out digital pulses and VIT signals located in the TV video vertical interval blanking bar much better than a X10 expander mode.

We will now use some square wave pulses to see how the delayed-sweep control setting operate. The scope trace in Fig. 4-36

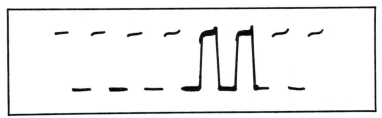

Fig. 4-37. Brighter pulses are A intensified.

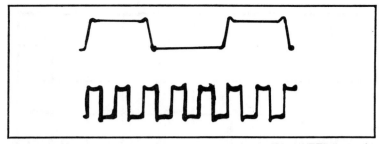

Fig. 4-38. The top trace is produced when the B DELAYED SWEEP button is depressed.

is a normal pulse as you would see it using the "A" time base generator. Now the trace in Fig. 4-37 was obtained by pushing the A-INTENSIFIED-BY-B TIME BASE GENERATOR button. Note that the two pulses are much brighter than the other pulses. These, of course, are the ones that are intensified. You may now rotate the DELAY TIME control and the brightened portion will move smoothly across the display screen. The brightened portion represents the delayed sweep and occurs according to the SEC/DIV. switch setting. The delayed-sweep speed is independent of the main sweep speed, and may be set to any speed equal to or faster than the main A time base sweep generator.

Now press the B DELAYED-SWEEP button and make sure that the intensified portion of the triggered waveform is now displayed across the entire scope screen as in Fig. 4-38. When using the delayed-sweep mode, another feature is that the trace does not have any jitter that usually occurs when you use the ×10 magnification mode on single time base oscilloscopes.

Chapter 5
Using Logic Probes for
Digital Circuit Troubleshooting

When troubleshooting circuits with analog devices, you need only test resistance, capacitance, or the turn-on voltages of components with two or three states. The total circuit may be quite complex, but each component in the circuit performs a simple task and its operation can be easily checked out. As shown in Fig. 5-1, each resistor, capacitor, diode and transistor can be tested by using a signal generator, VTVM, diode checker, or scope by performing the conventional troubleshooting techniques. With integrated circuits, however, these various components cannot be tested. Instead, it is necessary to troubleshoot the total circuit system.

The difference between discrete circuitry and today's digital ICs is the complexity of functions performed by these sophisticated devices. Unlike discrete devices, modern digital ICs perform complete and complex functions. Instead of observing simple characteristics, it is necessary to observe complex digital signals and decide if these signals are correct.

Verifying proper component operation now requires observing many inputs—note the 10 inputs of Fig. 5-1—while simultaneously observing 2 or more outputs. Thus, another difference between circuitry built from discrete components and digital IC's is the number of inputs and outputs for each component and the need to check each one simultaneously.

In addition to simulating test signals and complexity of functions at the component level, these ICs have caused a new degree of

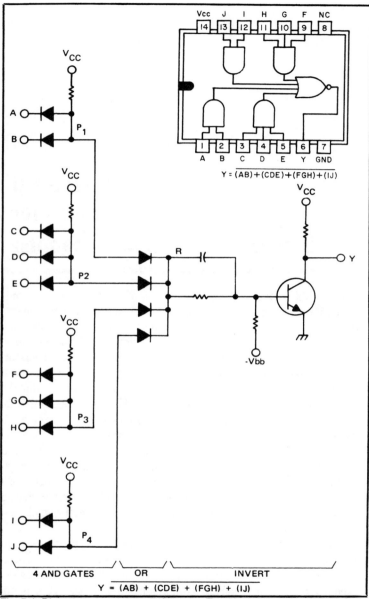

Fig. 5-1. Discrete versus integrated circuits. Troubleshooting circuits built from discrete components requires verifying relatively simple characteristics such as resistance, capacitance, or turn-on voltages. Today's circuits built from digital ICs require the verification of complex digital waveforms defined by the truth table of the IC.

124

complexity at the circuit level. If you have enough time, these circuits can be studied and their operations understood, but the technician just cannot spend that much time. Without going into all of the intricate operations of the circuit, it becomes necessary to have a technique for quickly testing each component rather than trying to isolate a failure to a particular circuit and testing for the expected signals.

In order to solve these problems and to make troubleshooting of digital circuits more efficient, it is necessary to take advantage of the digital nature of the signals involved. Tests and techniques designed to troubleshoot analog circuits do not take advantage of the digital signal and is less effective when used to troubleshoot digital circuits.

TTL LOGIC SIGNAL

A typical TTL pulse signal is shown in Fig. 5-2. This could well be any analog signal when viewed on an oscilloscope. The scope displays absolute voltage with respect to time. For digital pulses, however, absolute values are not important. A digital signal exists in one of two or three states—high, low, and an undefined or in-between level—each determined by a threshold voltage. It is the relative value of the signal voltage with respect to these thresholds that determines the state of the digital signal. And this digital state determines IC gate operation, not absolute levels. Note in Fig. 5-3 that if the signal is more than 2.4 volts, it is a high state. For a low state, the voltage must be below 0.8 volts. It is not important what the absolute level is as long as it is below this threshold. Therefore, when using the scope, you must always determine if the signal meets the threshold requirement for the desired digital state.

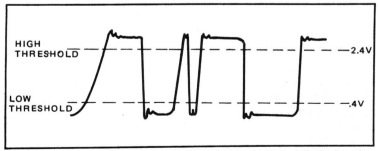

Fig. 5-2. Typical TTL pulse signal. In the digital world, the relative value of a signal voltage with respect to the threshold determines the operation of the circuit. A signal above the high threshold is in the high state. Whether the signal is 2.8V or 3.0V is unimportant to the operation of the circuit.

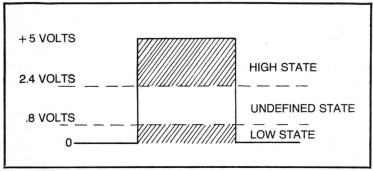

Fig. 5-3. TTL logic levels. 0 to 0.8 VDC is considered to be TTL low state. 2.4 to 5 VDC is considered to be TTL high state.

Each gate in a TTL logic family has a certain propagation delay time, rise time and fall time. The effects of these timing circuit operations are taken into account by the design engineer. Timing parameters rarely degrade or become marginal, so scope checks of these timing parameters contribute very little to the troubleshooting process.

The circuit in Fig. 5-4 illustrates a problem created by the TTL logic family. This is a TTL transistor totem pole device. In either the high or low state, it has a low impedance. In the low state, it appears as about 5 or 10 ohms to ground. This presents a problem for in-circuit stimulation. A device used to inject a pulse at a node that is driven by a TTL output must have sufficient power to override the low-impedance output state. Many pulsers used for troubleshooting do not have this capability, and the troubleshooter either has to cut the printed circuit runs or pull IC leads to pulse the circuit under test. These techniques are time-consuming and can damage other circuits.

A scope and traditional signal sources are inefficient for this reason. Since the diodes and transistors are packaged in the IC, use of diode checkers are also marginal. With the complexity of today's electronic circuits, it makes sense to find the most efficient solution to this problem. The oscilloscope, diode checkers and voltmeters should be used on analog circuits where they really shine and use instruments that take advantage of the digital nature of signals when checking digital circuitry.

WAYS THAT ICs MAY FAIL

To troubleshoot ICs, it is important to know what types of faults are found in these digital circuits. They can be placed into two main classes—those caused by internal IC faults and those caused by a circuit failure external to the IC chip.

There are four types of failures that can occur internally to an IC:

■ an open bond on either an input or output
■ a short between an input or output and V$_{cc}$ or ground
■ a short between two pins
■ a failure in the internal circuitry (often called the steering circuitry) of the IC.

In addition to these four failures inside an IC, there are four faults that can occur in the circuit external to the IC:

■ a short between a node and a V$_{cc}$ or ground
■ a short between two nodes
■ an open signal path
■ a failure of an analog component.

Let's now look at the effects these IC faults will have upon circuit operation. First, the failure for an open bond on either the input or output. In the case of an open output bond (Fig. 5-5), the inputs driven by that output are left to float. In TTL and DTL (diode transistor logic) circuits, a floating input rises to about 1.4 to 1.5 volts and usually has the same effect on circuit operation as a high logic level. Thus, an open output bond will cause all inputs driven by that output to float to a bad level since 1.5 volts is less than the high

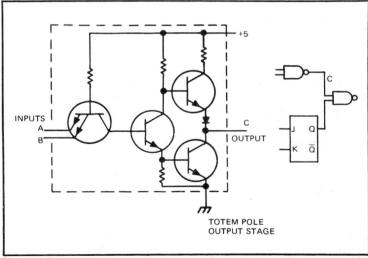

Fig. 5-4. To "jog" this gate, you must override the low-impedance totem pole output stage.

127

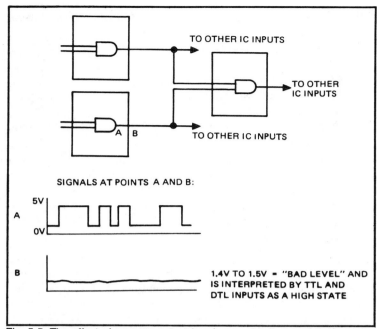

SIGNALS AT POINTS A AND B:

1.4V TO 1.5V = "BAD LEVEL" AND
IS INTERPRETED BY TTL AND
DTL INPUTS AS A HIGH STATE

Fig. 5-5. The effect of an open output bond upon circuit operation. An open output bond allows all inputs driven by that output to float to a bad level. This level is usually interpreted as a logic high state by the inputs. Thus the inputs driven by an open output bond will respond as though a static logic high signal was applied.

threshold level of 2.0 volts and greater than the low threshold level of 0.4 volts. In TTL and DTL, a floating input is seen as a high level. The effect will be that these inputs will respond to this bad level as though it were a static high signal.

With an open input bond (Fig. 5-6), you will find that the open circuit blocks the signal that drives the input from entering the IC chip. The input on the chip is thus allowed to float and will respond as though it were a static high signal. It is important to realize that because the open occurs on the input inside the IC, the digital signal driving this input will be unaffected by the open and will be detectable when looking at the input pin, such as at point A in Fig. 5-7. The effect will be to block this signal inside the IC and the resulting IC operation will be as though the input were a static high. A short between an input or output and V_{cc} or ground holds all signal lines connected to that input output either high (in the case of a short to V_{cc}) or low (if shorted to ground), as shown in Fig. 5-8. In many cases, this will cause expected signal activity at points beyond the short to disappear, which is catastrophic in terms of circuit operation.

A short between two pins is not as easy to analyze as a short to V_{cc} or ground. When two pins are shorted, the outputs driving those pins oppose each other when one attempts to pull the pins high while the other wants to pull them low as shown in Fig. 5-9. In this situation, the output that is attempting to go high will feed through the upper saturated transistor of its totem pole output stage while the output trying to go low will sink this current through the saturated lower transistor of its totem pole output stage. The net effect is that the short will be pulled to a low state by the saturated transistor to ground. Whenever both outputs attempt to go high or go low simultaneously, the shorted pins will respond properly. Whenever one output attempts to go low, though, the short will be constrained to be low.

The fourth internal failure of an IC is the steering circuitry within the IC, as shown in Fig. 5-9. This always causes the upper

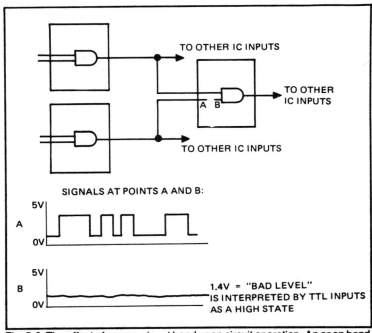

Fig. 5-6. The effect of an open input bond upon circuit operation. An open bond on an input has the effect of blocking the input signal from reaching the chip and allows the input of the chip to float to a bad level. Thus even though the signal can be viewed at an external point such as point A, the input of the chip responds to the bad level as though it were a static high level.

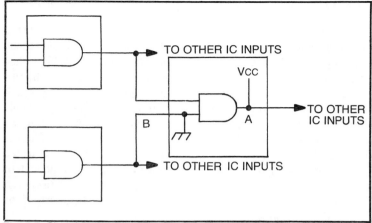

Fig. 5-7. Short between input or output and Vcc or ground.

transistor of the output totem pole to turn on—locking the output in the high state—or the lower transistor of the totem pole to turn on—locking the output to the low state. This failure blocks the signal flow and has a catastrophic effect upon circuit operation.

A short between a node and a Vcc or ground external to the IC or a short internal to the IC will appear the same. Both will cause the signal lines connected to the node to be either always high (for shorts to Vcc) or always low (for shorts to ground). When this type of failure is encountered only a very close "eye ball" examination of the circuit will reveal if the short is external to the IC.

An open signal path in the circuit has an effect similar to an open output bond driving the node, as shown in Fig. 5-10. All outputs to the right of the open will be allowed to float to a bad level and will appear as a static high level in circuit operation. Those inputs to the left of the open will be unaffected by the open and will respond as expected.

THE MODEL DP-50 B & K LOGIC PROBE

The B & K digital probe is designed for fast analysis of digital circuits and is compatible with TTL, DTL, RTL, CMOS, MOS and other solid-state circuitry. Three LED indicators at the probe tip display pulse presence high and high 1 and low 0 logic states. An incorrect logic level or an open pin is indicated by the absence of a lighted pulse LED. Two switches allow you to select TTL or CMOS logic thresholds and pulse stretch mode or memory modes. In the pulse stretch mode, short duration pulses are stretched for a clear

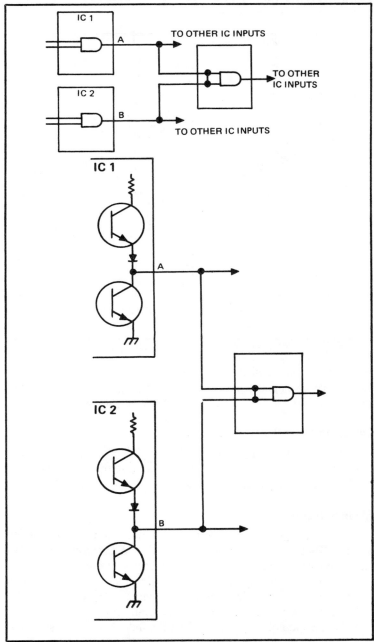

Fig. 5-8. Effect of a short between two pins of an IC.

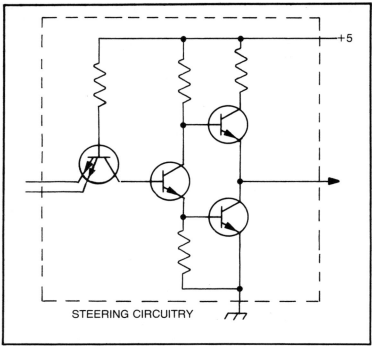

Fig. 5-9. Failure of an internal steering circuit within an IC.

visual indication. In the memory mode, a single digital pulse causes a LED to remain lighted until reset. This permits you to freeze the display of digital action. The B & K DP-50 is shown in Fig. 5-11.

Threshold Level Operation

Set the THRESHOLD switch to the TTL position to select the correct threshold level for TTL, DTL, etc. Use the CMOS position for MOS and CMOS digital circuits.

Mode Selection

The MODE switch provides pulse detection in either pulse stretch (PULSE position) or memory (MEM position) modes. In the pulse stretch mode the PULSE indicator lights a minimum of 200 milliseconds in response to each single pulse of 20 nanoseconds or greater duration. If the input pulse is short, it is stretched to 200 milliseconds to assure a high-visibility flash on the LED.

In the memory mode, the PULSE indicator remains lighted after the first pulse or logic transition until it is reset by moving the

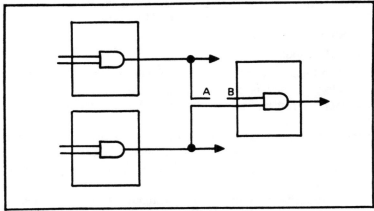

Fig. 5-10. Effect of an open circuit external to an IC.

mode switch to the PULSE position. To use the memory mode, set the MODE switch to the PULSE position and then connect the probe tip to the point being checked. This initial contact will cause

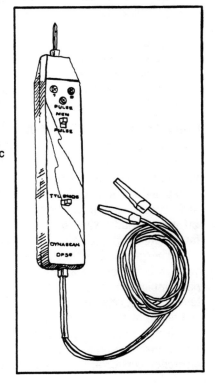

Fig. 5-11. B & K model DP-50 logic probe.

the pulse indicator to flash. Following the initial flash, move the MODE switch to the MEM position. The probe is now ready to operate in the memory mode.

Using The Probe

The 1 indicator will remain lighted only during the time period when logic level 1 is present at the probe tip. Similarly, the 0 indicator will remain lighted only during the time period when the logic level 0 is present at the probe tip. The PULSE indicator will light as the result of a transition in logic levels. Thus, typical operating situations may be encountered as follows:

- ■ With the probe tip touching symmetrical pulses, the 0 and 1 indicators will both be lighted at one-half brilliance, and the PULSE indicator will be lighted at full brilliance.
- ■ With the probe tip touching a positive-going, high-speed pulse of a short duty cycle, the 0 and PULSE indicators will be lighted, and the 1 indicator will be partially lighted on duty cycles greater than 10 percent.
- ■ With the probe tip touching negative-going, high-speed pulses of a short duty cycle, the 1 and PULSE indicators will be lighted. The 0 indicator will be partially lighted on duty cycles that are greater than 10 percent.
- ■ When only the PULSE indicator is illuminated, system noise or pulses above 50 MHz are indicated.
- ■ With the probe touching an open pin or an incorrect logic level (a voltage within the deadband), indicator will light.

LOGIC PROBES BY CONTINENTAL SPECIALTIES

The logic probe, like the Continental Specialties (now Global Specialties Corporation) LP-1 shown in Fig. 5-12, detects, memorizes and displays logic levels, pulses and voltage transients in mixed and single logic family systems. It detects out-of-tolerance logic signals, open-circuit nodes, as well as transient events down to 50 nanoseconds while providing the user with an instant easily interpreted high-intensity LED readout.

The probe tip of the LP-1 is connected to a dual-threshold window comparator and bipolar edge detector. The window comparator bias network sets the LOGIC "1" and LOGIC "0" threshold levels. The levels are fixed in the DTL/TTL mode (2.25 volts and 0.8 volts) in the CMOS/HTL mode.

The bipolar edge detector responds to both positive and negative transitions and drives a pulse stretcher circuit. The pulse stretcher converts level transitions as well as narrow pulses to

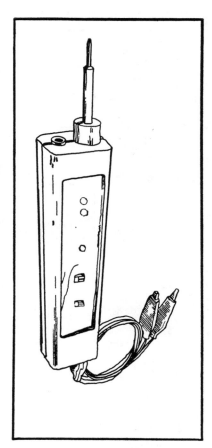

Fig. 5-12. Continental Specialties
LP-1 logic probe.

one-third of a second in length that drive one of the three readout
LEDs. In the memory mode, the output of the edge detector is fed
to a latching flip-flop.

Using The Logic Probe

Connect the clip leads of the logic probe to the power supply of
the circuit under test. Then set the LOGIC FAMILY switch to
DTL/TTL or CMOS/HTL and the MEMORY/PULSE switch to
the PULSE position. Touch the probe tip to the circuit node to be
analyzed. The three display LEDs on the probe body will instantly
provide a reading of the signal activity at the node. The memory
mode of the LP-1 is used to detect, store and display low-repetition
rate or single-shot pulses as well as transient events, even when an
observer is not around when they occur.

LED STATES			INPUT SIGNAL	
HIGH	LO	PULSE		
○	●	○	o————	LOGIC "0" NO PULSE ACTIVITY
●	○	○	o————	LOGIC "1" NO PULSE ACTIVITY
○	○	○	————	**ALL LEDS OFF** 1. TEST POINT IS AN OPEN CIRCUIT. 2. OUT OF TOLERANCE SIGNAL. 3. PROBE NOT CONNECTED TO POWER. 4. NODE OR CIRCUIT NOT POWERED.
●	●	*	o⊓⊓⊓	THE SHARED BRIGHTNESS OF THE HI AND LO LEDS INDICATE A 50% DUTY CYCLE AT THE TEST POINT.(<100KHz)
○	○	*	o⊓⊓⊓⊓⊓	HIGH FREQUENCY SQUARE WAVE (>100KHz) AT TEST NODE. AS THE HIGH FREQUENCY SIGNALS DUTY CYCLE SHIFTS FROM A SQUARE WAVE TO EITHER A HIGH OR LOW DUTY CYCLE PULSE TRAIN EITHER THE LO OR HI LED WILL BECOME ACTIVATED.
○	●	*	o‖‖‖‖	LOGIC "0" PULSE ACTIVITY PRESENT POSITIVE GOING PULSES SINCE HI LED NOT "ON" PULSE TRAIN DUTY CYCLE IS LOW RE < 15%. IF THE DUTY CYCLE WERE INCREASED ABOVE 15% HI LED WOULD START TO TURN ON.
●	○	*	o⫿⫿⫿	LOGIC "1" PULSE ACTIVITY PRESENT NEGATIVE GOING PULSES, SINCE LO LED NOT "ON" PULSE TRAIN DUTY CYCLE IS HIGH RE >85% IF THE DUTY CYCLE WERE REDUCED TO <85% "LO" LED WOULD START TO TURN ON.

● LED ON
○ LED OFF
* BLINKING LED

Fig. 5-13. Chart for interpreting the LED readouts of the probes.

A chart for interpreting the action of the logic probe LEDs is shown in Fig. 5-13. The relation of probe tip voltage to probe power supply voltage is shown in the Fig. 5-14.

Powering Up The Probe

The LP-1 is protected against excessive voltage and reverse voltage on its power leads. Connect the black lead to the common (–) and the red clip lead to plus (+) V_{cc}. In order to minimize the possibility of power supply spikes or other spurious signals from affecting the operation of the probe, connect the power leads as close to the node to be tested as possible.

Memory/Pulse Switch - Pulse Position

Each time the input signal changes state, the pulse LED is activated for 0.3 seconds. When observing low-frequency, low-duty cycle signals, the pulse LED provides a quick indication of the pulse activity at the node under test. By observing the HI and LO LEDs, the phase of the pulse train can be determined. If the HI LED is on, the signal is normally high and pulsing low, and so on. High-frequency signals cause the pulse LED to flash at a 3-Hz rate.

Memory/Pulse Switch - Memory Position

The LP-1 probe contains a pulse memory flip-flop that catches and holds (memorizes) level transitions or pulses as narrow as 50 nanoseconds. The memory is activated by either positive or negative level transitions.

To set the probe for catching and memorizing an event, just touch the probe tip to the node under test with the switch in the MEMORY position. The next event that occurs will activate the pulse LED and latch it on. To reset and rearm the memory, move the MEM/PULSE switch to the PULSE position and then return it to the MEM position.

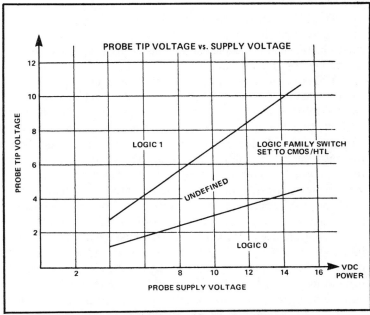

Fig. 5-14. Voltage relation chart for the LP-1 logic probe.

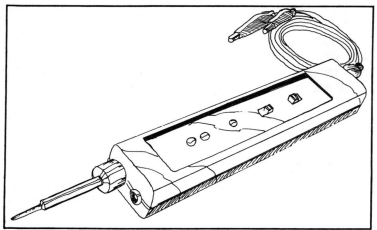
Fig. 5-15. Continental Specialties LP-3 logic probe.

NOTE: When arming the memory, the probe tip must be in contact with the test point in question. If the memory is armed with the tip floating (not connected), the memory will be activated when the tip makes contact, thus yielding a false readout.

Fast Pulse Catcher

The LP-3 model probe shown in Fig. 5-15 contains a unique and highly sensitive pulse detecting system capable of catching pulses faster than 10 nanoseconds. This insures capture of glitches and spikes for all logic families: TTL, DTL, RTL and CMOS.

The pulse detector circuit consists of a level sensitive broad-band amplifier coupled to a high-speed pulse stretching monostable multivibrator. This circuit is capable of firing on both positive and negative transitions. The pulse stretcher enables a 100-millisecond oscillator and LED driver circuit that produces a visual indication of the pulse catch. The oscillator can also be switched into a bistable mode in order to catch a pulse for memory. This technology allows you to catch and display hidden spikes and glitches that many scopes and logic probes will not detect. Basic rf troubleshooting techniques are required as you try to locate these fast spikes and pulses.

The ground lead of the LP-3 must be used. Ground lines must be as short as possible. Connect the ground lead of the probe as close to the test point as possible. In the case of an IC, clip the ground lead directly to the IC ground pin. The ground lead can supply the signal return and negative power line path for the logic probe, and will help prevent ground loops.

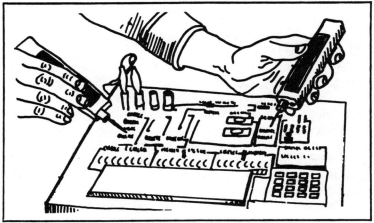

Fig. 5-16. The LP-2 and the DP-2 digital pulser probe in action.

DP-1 PULSE GENERATOR PROBE

Figure 5-16 shows the E & L Instruments model MMD-1 microprocessor trainer in the process of being checked by using Continental Specialties LP-2 logic test probe and the DP-1 pulse

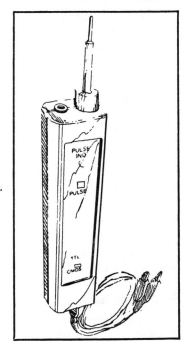

Fig. 5-17. The DP-1 digital pulser probe.

generator IC probe tester. This completely automatic pulse generator may be used for troubleshooting the more sophisticated microprocessor and other family of digital/logic circuits. Figure 5-17 shows the DP-1.

By obtaining its power from the circuit under test, the DP-1 self-adjusts the amplitude of its output pulse to the input requirements of the circuit to be tested. When the pulser tip is connected to the circuit node to be tested, the auto polarity sensing system of the probe selects the sink or power source pulse required to activate the test point. Simply depress the push button once to produce a clean, bounce-free pulse. When the pushbutton is held down for more than one second, the unit produces a pulse train at a 100 pulses-per-second rate.

The pulser has a fail-safe feature, which permits an overvoltage condition up to 25 volts. Other built-in protection will withstand a reverse voltage to 50 volts and allows the unit to pulse continuously into a short circuit. The DP-1 allows the service technician all the versatility of a laboratory quality pulse generator without the need to set pulse levels or switch to complement the output pulses.

Autopolarity Sensing

The pulser contains a circuit that automatically selects the sink or source pulse needed by the circuit under test. By comparing the test point voltage between pulses to the center of the dead zone voltage for the IC under test, the DP-1 senses whether a "0" level is present and outputs a "1" pulse, or if a "1" level is present it outputs a "0" pulse.

The autopolarity sensing level is checked after each pulse to allow for changes of state after a trigger pulse. This permits the DP-1 to trigger on RS flip-flops supplying alternate, sink and source pulses to cross-coupled junctions to keep the flip-flop toggled. See Fig. 5-18. This function allows you to jump from point to point on a circuit board without regard to the logic state of the test point.

Tri-state Output

The DP-1 is a tri-state output device with a minimum of 300K ohm loading when not being pulsed. This allows all logic ICs, including CMOS, to be unaffected by pulse loading between pulses.

Single-Shot Mode

By depressing and releasing the push button, a single, debounced pulse is produced at the output. The pushbutton may be

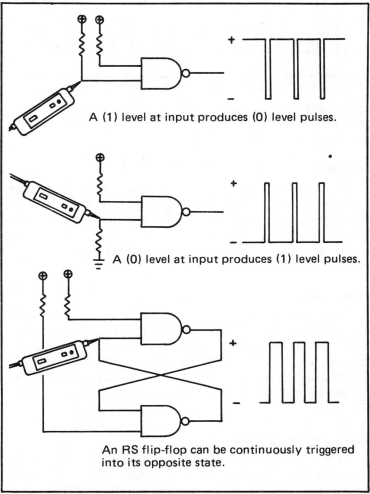

A (1) level at input produces (0) level pulses.

A (0) level at input produces (1) level pulses.

An RS flip-flop can be continuously triggered into its opposite state.

Fig. 5-18. Autosensing setup.

depressed as rapidly as needed to produce a controlled stream of single pulses. Note Fig. 5-19.

The pushbutton must be released within one second in order to remain in the single-shot mode. The LED flashes once for each single shot pulse that is produced.

Continuous Mode

When the pushbutton is depressed, a single pulse is instantly produced. If the button is held down for more than one second, the

Fig. 5-19. Stream of digital pulses.

output switches from single-shot to continuous mode, which produces a train of pulses at 100 pulses per second rate. The LED stays lit for continuous mode operation.

TTL Mode

When the slide switch is in the TTL position, the output pulse width is 1.5 microseconds. The pulse rise time is less than 10 nanoseconds with a maximum 500-nanosecond storage and fall time for one TTL load. Storage and fall time decreases as TTL loading increases. In the TTL mode, the output pulse can sink or source 100 mA or 60 TTL loads.

CMOS Mode

When the slide switch is in the CMOS position, the output pulse is 10 microseconds. This allows ample time for the slowest CMOS devices to be activated. The pulse rise time is less than 100 nanoseconds, with an 8 nanosecond storage and fall time for 100K ohm load resistance. In the CMOS mode, the output pulse can sink or source 50 mA to a logic "1" or a logic "0" level for any V_{cc} from 4 to 18 volts.

Hooking Up and Using the DP-1

The power cable of the DP-1 not only feeds power to the unit, but acts as the return path for the output pulse. In order to decrease common moding and ground loops, clip the power cable lead as close to the pulsing point as possible. When power is first applied to the pulser, the LED will light and stay on for about one second. After the LED has gone off, the pulser is ready to use.

In most cases there is no need to use the ground clip, as the unit produces a crisp pulse under normal conditions. However, the ground lead does help the pulser sink larger currents and can reduce pulse storage time.

If the ground lead is to be used, do not hook up the black power lead. Both ground returns can cause common moding and ground loops which may produce false triggering in the circuit under test.

142

The DP-1 is an extremely effective tool to help troubleshoot digital/logic circuits. In many cases, it is much more useful than using an oscilloscope.

Figure 5-20 shows the hookup for checking out a 7490 decade counter using a pulser and a logic monitor. The pulser CMOS/TTL switch is set to TTL, and the pulser tip is connected to the zero set input of the 7490. The logic monitor is clamped onto the 7490 to display all the logic states of the counter simultaneously.

Depressing the pushbutton once puts a zero pulse into the 7490 and clears all the outputs to zero. The pulser can now be applied to the clock input and single step or jog the 7490 through its decade cycle.

When the counter is pulsed, all four outputs can be seen changing state, while simultanously monitoring the power supply input, clock inputs and clear lines. This is one advantage of the logic

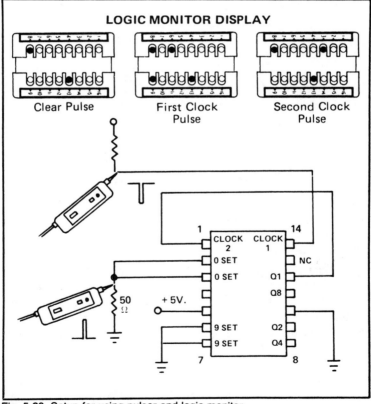

Fig. 5-20. Setup for using pulser and logic monitor.

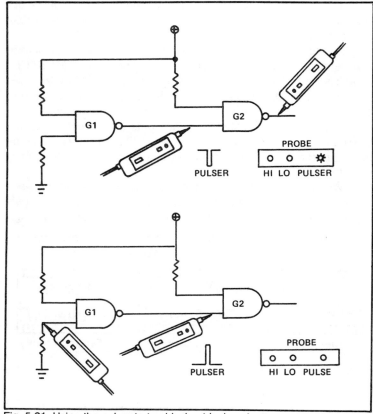

Fig. 5-21. Using the pulser to troubleshoot logic gates.

monitor pulser approach over the scope, which at best can only monitor one or two points at a time.

TROUBLESHOOTING GATES

Although logic monitors work very well on counter latches and flip-flops, they are basically static devices and cannot display the pulsers narrow output pulse. When troubleshooting gating and decoding systems, a logic probe is needed for its pulse stretching abilities. The narrowest pulse of the DP-1 can be caught and held for one-third of a second, while the HI/LO LEDs indicate that the node under test is high pulsing low or low pulsing high.

In Fig. 5-21A, a two-gate circuit is under test. The output of G1 is held high, causing the output of G2 to be low. By applying the pulser to the output of G1, the pulser overrides the output state of

G1 and puts a train of zero pulses into the gate of G2. The logic probe connected to the output of G2 has its low LED on, but then the pulse LED starts flashing. This shows the gate is passing the input pulses in proper polarity. In Fig. 5-21B, the probe is moved to the output of G1, and the pulser is applied to the low gate input. The pulser now produces a series of one pulses when the pushbutton is held down; however, the pulse LED of the probe does not respond, indicating a defective gate.

Logic Probe Jogging Test Technique

With the high fanout of the pulser, it has the ability of overriding the output level set by a gate by applying the needed input pulse to the circuitry under test. This sets the stage for system troubleshooting by using the jogging method. A digital system can be deactivated by disconnecting the clock of the system and replacing its pulses with those of the pulser. The complete system may now be jogged through its cycle while different points of interest in the system may be displayed with logic probes, logic monitors or even an oscilloscope.

Several logic monitors may be used simultaneously to display the movement of a pulse from IC to IC, or show the response of several gates to the same stimuli. The distinct advantages of this method become quite evident once you have put this method into operation. You will probably find that the pulser and logic probes are an extremely effective way to troubleshoot digital/logic circuits and gates. With this technique, you are able to jog a logic pulse through various gates for a FRAME-FREEZE-TIME or a slow-motion look at gate action.

Logic Troubleshooting Tips

- Make sure you understand how the logic device is supposed to operate.
- IC logic gates will very often become overheated when they are defective. Check the temperature of these logic ICs.
- Try not to replace any components until you have zeroed in on the trouble.
- Use the logic test probe for signal tracing and the logic pulser probe for signal injection.
- Have it well established in your mind what the circuit signal flow and the logic levels should be.

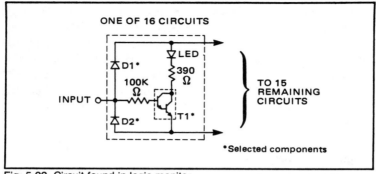

Fig. 5-22. Circuit found in logic monitor.

■ When troubleshooting with the logic probe, always touch the probe tip to the IC terminal leads. Avoid the probe tip test at the IC socket.

■ Use a DVM to measure the very critical voltages found in all logic circuits.

■ Remove and install MOS microprocessor chips and all logic devices very carefully. Be on the alert for any static buildup.

LOGIC MONITORS

A logic monitor test clip can be used to simultaneously display the static and dynamic logic states of DTL, TTL or CMOS 14-pin and 16-pin digital dual-in-line ICs. With the logic monitor, each IC lead is measured by 1 of 16 independent binary/optical sensors. When one of the input voltages exceeds the 2V threshold, the LED corresponding to the activated input pin is turned on. Inputs below the threshold or uncommitted (floating) do not activate their corresponding LEDs. A built-in power seeking gating network locates the most positive and negative voltages applied to the IC under test. This network then feeds them to the internal buffered amplifiers and LED drivers.

Logic Monitor Circuit Operation

All of the 16 circuits for Continental Specialties LM-1 logic monitor are identical and act as buffer amplifiers, comparators and LED drivers. Selected diodes and Darlington transistors assure the device threshold level and LED drive capacity. Figure 5-22 shows the circuit.

When any of the remaining 14 input points is connected to a signal source that exceeds 2V, the Darlington transistors conduct and turn on the LED in its collector. The 100K ohm resistor in series with the base of each transistor prevents loading of the circuit under test. The 390-ohm collector resistor limits the LED and LM-1 current drain from the power supply system of the IC that is being tested.

Using the Clip-on Test Monitor

The logic monitor can be clamped onto any digital IC with up to 16 pins, as shown in Fig. 5-23. Grooved pin guides ensure positive connections between test monitor contacts and the IC leads. Static and dynamic logic levels appear on the test LEDs for optical readout. Once clamped in place on the IC, the logic monitor test is automatic. The V_{cc} or the most positive IC terminal will be indicated by a continuously lighted LED. The least positive or uncommitted and logic 0 IC terminals will appear as unlighted LEDs.

By reducing the system or IC input signal rate to 10 Hz or less, you will be able to see each logic state of the IC under investigation. Troubleshooting with the logic monitor requires a knowledge of the IC logic pin outs. For example, consider a quad and its gate config-

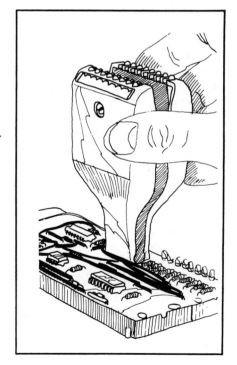

Fig. 5-23. How a logic monitor clamps on the IC.

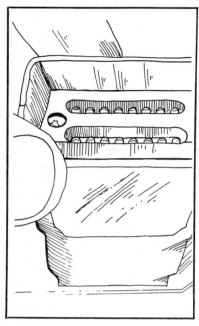

Fig. 5-24. Hewlett-Packard HP-548A logic clip probe.

uration. If the output pin of one of the gates is constantly low (LED off) and gate inputs are not simultaneously high, either the gate outputs are not simultaneously high, either the gate output is shorted to ground internally or a short exists on the lines fed by the gate output.

Other Logic Monitor Applications

During the design, layout and testing phases of a new logic system, the designer has control of the variables of the system (clock, power supplies, I/O interfaces, etc.) and can easily isolate ICs for detailed investigation with the logic monitor. When a logic block needs an additional gate, inverter, flip-flop, register, etc., the logic monitor can quickly show you where unused logic gates are located within the system. Nonfunctioning components can easily be located and replaced. Long-term testing of individual modules can be implemented by clipping the logic monitor onto the questionable IC. This is a good check for locating intermittent troubles.

Because the entire IC can be monitored simultaneously, direct and fast visual correlation of IC inputs and outputs simplifies and expedites signal tracing data transfer and system fault-finding operations. System and IC reactions to power supply changes and noise testing are other application areas that make the logic monitor an almost indispensable troubleshooting and design instrument. Mixed logic design DTL, TTL and CMOS, where designers take advantage of each logic family, and also TTL or HTL outputs, are naturals for the logic monitors.

Use the logic clip when dealing with multiple PC board systems. Placing one logic clip on the inputs or outputs of the driving/receiving board and one on the board under test enables you to observe the results of any modification or stimulation on one board while making other circuit adjustments.

HEWLETT-PACKARD MODEL 548A LOGIC CLIP

The H-P Model 548A logic clip shown in Fig. 5-24 has internal self-seeking logic circuitry so that it can be placed on a device upside-down or right side-up. The clip locates the supply and ground pins and then starts indicating the state of all pins. The buffered inputs of the clip draw less than 15 microamps from signal pins, ensuring that circuit loading will not usually occur.

TEMPERATURE PROBE APPLICATIONS

The B & K model TP-28 temperature probe shown in the Fig. 5-25 is a temperature-sensitive voltage generator that can be used with most digital or analog voltmeters as an electronic thermometer. The voltmeter must have an input impedance of 10K ohms or

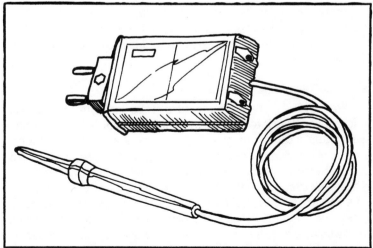

Fig. 5-25. B & K model TP-28 temperature probe.

Table 5-1. Voltmeter Conversions for the TP-28 Temperature Probe.

| VOLTAGE READING RANGES | | | | | | TEMPERATURE °C OR °F |
| DIGITAL VOLTMETER | | ANALOG VOLTMETER | | | | |
1-VOLT	10-VOLT	0-5 VOLT	0-1 VOLT	0-1 5 VOLT	0-3 VOLT OR 0-5 VOLT	SWITCH-SELECTABLE
	03 02				3 02	302°
	02 50				2 50	250°
	02 12				2 12	212°
	02 00				2 00	200°
1 999					1 99	199 9°
1 500				1 50	1 50	150 0°
1 000			1 00	1 00	1 00	100 0°
0 500			0 50	0 50		50 0°
0 320		500	0 32	0 32		32 0°
0 250		320	0 25	0 25		25 0°
0 100		250	0 10	0 10		10 0°
0 000		100	0 00	0 00		0 0°
- 0 100		0 00	- 0 10	- 0 10		- 10 0°
- 0 250		- 100	- 0 25	- 0 25		- 25 0°
- 0 500		- 250	- 0 50	- 0 50		- 50 0°
- 0 580		- 500	- 0 58	- 0 58		- 58 0°
°F °C APPROXIMATELY 1 VOLT						REPLACE BATTERY

more. The meter should offer good accuracy and resolution in the 0 to 3-volt ranges. The 3½-digit B & K model 2830 digital multimeter is an ideal companion for this temperature probe. With an autopolarity digital multimeter, the negative sign is automatically displayed for temperature below zero degrees. Refer to Table 5-1 for the conversion of the voltmeter voltage readings to temperature.

The TP-28 measures the temperature at the tip of the probe. It can thus be used to measure atmospheric temperature, can be immersed to measure the temperature of liquids, or held against a part for surface temperature measurements. The TP-28 probe also has several nonelectronic applications, such as measuring the temperature of walls, floors and ceilings to determine where additional insulation is needed; locating cold air leaks; and measuring the temperature of liquids, such as water and solutions used in photo processing.

Using The Temperature Probe

You will find that the temperature probe has many applications in electronics. Use it to monitor the ambient temperature at various points within a cabinet of operating equipment and within temperature chambers during environmental tests. In the design lab, it can be used to verify temperature difference between a transistor and its heat sink to check on the amount of heat transfer. Case temperatures can be used to evaluate biasing. The probe can be used to quickly check out the banks of ICs found on RAM boards. A shorted RAM would be very hot, while a cold one would indicate an inoperative one. Figure 5-26 shows the TP-28 probe being used with a

Fig. 5-26. B & K temperature probe in operation.

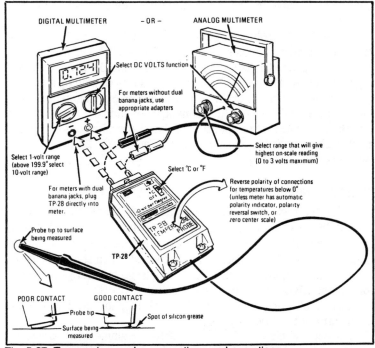

Fig. 5-27. Temperature probe connections and operations.

151

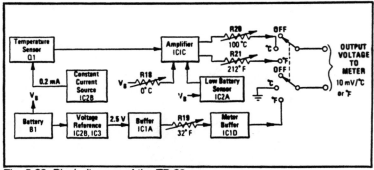

Fig. 5-28. Block diagram of the TP-28.

B&K model 277 FET-VOM to check temperature of a micro-processor chip.

Heat dissipation qualities of heat sinks and components can be evaluated as conservative or marginal. The probe can be used to determine oscillator temperature/frequency drift and measure temperature compensation parameters. The temperature probe provides a voltage proportional to temperature which may be applied to a chart recorder for long-term temperature measurements.

The TP-28 probe can be a very valuable test instrument for digital electronics troubleshooting. Figure 5-27 shows the connections of the probe to the various voltmeters and the proper operating techniques. The probe can locate hot spots caused by shorts or partial shorts. Lack of heat indicates inoperative components. It can also test thermal devices. An incoming inspection department could use the probe to test temperature-related specifications of components. The circuit block diagram of the model TP-28 temperature probe is shown in Fig. 5-28.

HANDLING MOS DEVICES

Service technicians must use caution while testing and installing MOS IC devices that may cause damage with static electricity arcs. Some of the solid-state devices now used in many minicomputers and color TV chassis can be damaged with a static discharge. You will now find the MOS IC used in a large number of consumer products. MOS transistors are small and use little power, thus thousands of them can be placed into an IC package that only use milliwatts of total power.

Most technicians are familiar with the single MOS transistor used for rf amplification in TV and FM receivers. MOS ICs are now being used in complete electronic tuning systems. They provide on-screen display of channel numbers plus time, and can remember user-programmed channels. TV games and minicomputers use MOS circuits extensively.

The low-power feature of MOS circuits can cause problems when you have to replace them. They are very sensitive to voltage spikes and static electricity. MOS transistors are made with a thin insulating layer (oxide) sandwiched between a gate electrode (metal) and a silicon subtrate (semiconductor). Because the oxide layer is so thin, voltages applied to the gate can influence the properties of the underlying silicon, thus controlling current between the source and drain. Part of the low-power feature arises because there is almost no DC current flow required at the gate electrode.

Some engineers claim that the major cause of failures in MOS ICs is due to breakdown of the gate oxide. Because some static electricity sparks are near 10,000 volts, this will most certainly destroy the device when discharged through a gate electrode of an MOS transistor. Even though static electricity currents are small, the only discharge path is through the gate oxide, and even small

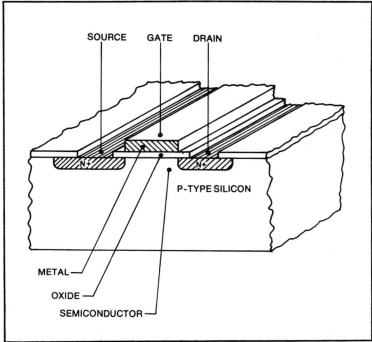

Fig. 5-29. Cross section of an MOS device.

currents that pass through the oxide will cause a failure. Note the cross-section of a MOS device in Fig. 5-29.

Inside the MOS IC, most transistors have a gate electrode driven by other MOS devices and are protected to some degree from external static electricity. The transistors at the input and output connections are the most susceptible to static damage. To protect input/output devices, protection networks are built inside the IC. These networks usually consist of diodes which bleed off static charges to ground or power supply pins and series resistors which protect the gate during the bleed-off process. These internal devices improve resistance to static damage but are limited by their small size. Some static shocks are sufficient to burn out the protection networks as well as the MOS gate oxide.

Some special techniques have been developed to protect ICs from static shock. ICs can be shipped in metal or conductive plastic coated tubes or trays. Often ICs will have their leads inserted into a black conductive foam or into aluminum foil. Conductive foam and plastic envelopes or metal-lined trays are used to transport circuit boards containing static-sensitive ICs.

MOS Handling Procedures

So as not to blow out MOS devices, keep in mind that you should avoid using any static-producing accessories. The following procedures are effective in reducing static shock:

- Just before touching any component or module, touch the metal chassis to make sure your body is not statically charged.
- While removing circuit boards or modules from the chassis, place them on a conductive surface, such as aluminum foil, and not on the bench.
- Touch the metal chassis just before picking up a module or component for installation. A MOS conductive work bench is shown in Fig. 5-30.
- When removing or replacing ICs, soldering irons with grounded tips must be used.
- Some solder suckers generate static charges when triggered on and should not be used. Even while the IC being removed is defective, a solder sucker can generate enough static to damage other components on the board. Antistatic solder suckers are essential for IC removal.
- Replacement MOS ICs are packaged in conductive foam or with aluminum foil. Do not remove the IC from its

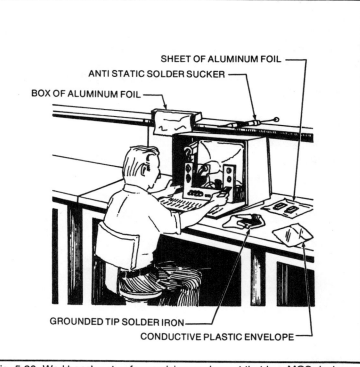

SHEET OF ALUMINUM FOIL

ANTI STATIC SOLDER SUCKER

BOX OF ALUMINUM FOIL

GROUNDED TIP SOLDER IRON

CONDUCTIVE PLASTIC ENVELOPE

Fig. 5-30. Workbench setup for servicing equipment that has MOS devices.

protective package until it is ready for use. Before removing the IC, touch the conductive foam to the chassis or circuit board in which it is to be inserted. This can be done by touching the board with one hand and the conductive package with the other.

■ Try to minimize motion when handling ICs out of the package. Clothes will even generate static electricity when brushed against other objects.

■ Do not use freon-propelled sprays on circuit boards or chassis. Freon spray will generate static electricity. Even when an IC is in a protective package or installed in a circuit board, freon spray can generate static electricity which may damage internal components not directly connected to the IC pins.

■ Defective components should be returned in a conductive package, not in plastic boxes or plastic envelopes. Aluminum foil is an effective packaging material.

155

Although these tips are for MOS ICs, all IC types can be damaged by static arcs and sparks. The more complex ICs tend to make integrated circuits even more sensitive to static damage, although they promise a fantastic future of improved performance and additional features in consumer products. The effectiveness of ICs depends a lot on the ever increasing skill and knowledge of those who troubleshoot these devices.

Chapter 6
Selected ICs Found
In Consumer Products

Some of the ICs found in the modern color TV chassis are almost as sophisticated as a microprocessor chip. In the first portion of this chapter you will see what some of the functions of these ICs are in a General Electric AA color chassis. These integrated circuits are found in the i-f and video section, synchronous demodulator, sound system, chroma chip and horizontal processor. Tips on video signal troubleshooting will then be covered.

The next section will give details on chips found in the Zenith triple-plus color chassis. This will include the master scan oscillator and vertical countdown circuits. Coverage then continues to stereo multiplex ICs and ceramic filters. The chapter concludes with some tips for signal tracing and troubleshooting analog IC chips.

GE COLOR TV AA CHASSIS

The functional block diagram for the GE AA chassis, shown in Fig. 6-1, illustrates the conventional solid-state design. The chassis has four ICs and we will look at some of these unique circuits in more detail.

IC 120 - I-F and Video Chip

The IC 120 chip contains not only the i-f amplifier, but the agc, afc and video detector functions as well. Two of these IC functions are not a common TV design. The agc circuit is not keyed, and the video is a synchronous demodulator.

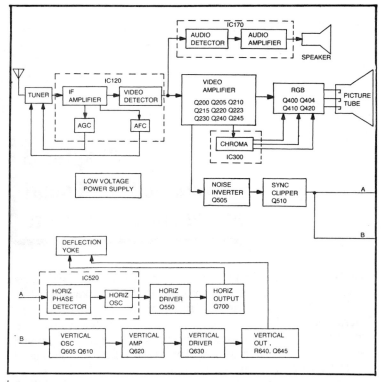

Fig. 6-1. Block diagram of a General Electric AA chassis.

AGC Operation. The principle components in the agc system are contained in IC 120, shown in the Fig. 6-2. This is not a keyed agc system, so horizontal keying pulses are not required. Connections to the video detector and the i-f amplifier are made internally. The only peripheral components are the rf agc network, connected to pins 3 and 4, and the agc filter components, which are connected to pin 14. The voltage on pin 14 is a good check point to measure i-f-agc. A value of 10 volts indicates maximum i-f gain, and 5 volts corresponds to minimum signal gain.

A diode keeps the voltage from going below about 4 volts. This prevents a condition called *agc lock out* in which rf gain is at a maximum, i-f gain is at a minimum, and there is no recognizable video output.

When the rf agc output is near 9 volts, the gain of the tuner is at maximum. As the voltage is reduced toward zero, the gain of the tuner is decreased.

Reference Amplifier. The function of the reference amplifier is to filter and to limit the amplitude of the 45.75-MHz modulated signal to provide an almost pure fundamental 45.75-MHz signal as a carrier reference for the synchronous demodulator. The i-f signal is fed to the differential amplifier Q2 and Q3 through Q1 and Q4. The IC 120 reference amplifier circuit is shown in Fig. 6-3. The collector load of the differential amplifier is formed by the high-Q tuned filter L1 and C1. Because of the high Q, the filter tends to respond only to the 45.75-MHz frequency and not the sideband frequencies. Diodes D1 and D2 are connected across the filters to limit the amplitude of the reference signal. As a result, the output is a nearly constant amplitude 45.75-MHz signal.

Synchronous Demodulator. In Fig. 6-4, Q7 is a constant current source. Q1 and Q2 form a differential amplifier, and Q3 through Q6 are carrier-operated switches. The differential amplifier is fed by the i-f amplifier, and the carrier-operated switches are fed by the reference amplifier.

When the positive half cycles of the amplitude-modulated carrier appear at the base of Q1, it increases conduction. At the same time the in-phase, clipped carrier signal at the base of Q3 switches

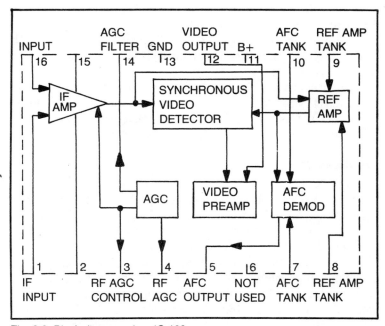

Fig. 6-2. Block diagram of an IC 120.

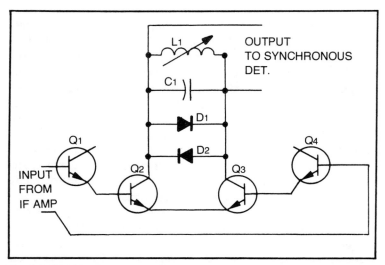

Fig. 6-3. IC 120 reference amplifier.

this transistor on, causing current flow through RT to increase. No current will flow through Q4; it is turned off by the reverse-phase, clipped carrier.

When the negative half cycle appears at the base of Q1, it decreases conduction, causing Q2 to increase conduction. The reverse-phase carrier turns Q4 on, causing the current through R1 to increase. No current will flow through Q3 since the in-phase carrier pulse is negative at this time.

The current flow through R1 increases for both negative and positive half cycles of the carrier, producing a waveform, as shown in Fig. 6-4D. This waveform represents the amplitude modulation which we desired to recover from the incoming signal.

170 Sound Chip

The IC 170 chip is a complete audio system for the GE AA chassis. It contains a 4.5-MHz amplifier, quadrature detector, electronic attenuator and audio amplifier. In addition, it contains voltage regulating, current limiting and thermal overload circuitry, as shown in the Fig. 6-5 block diagram.

The input to the 4.5-MHz amplifier is at pin 10. The amplifier is connected internally to the quadrature detector. The qual coil is connected to pins 14 and 15. The de-emphasis/tone control network is connected to pin 16. The electronic attenuator is controlled by the voltage from the VOLUME control, which is connected to pin

160

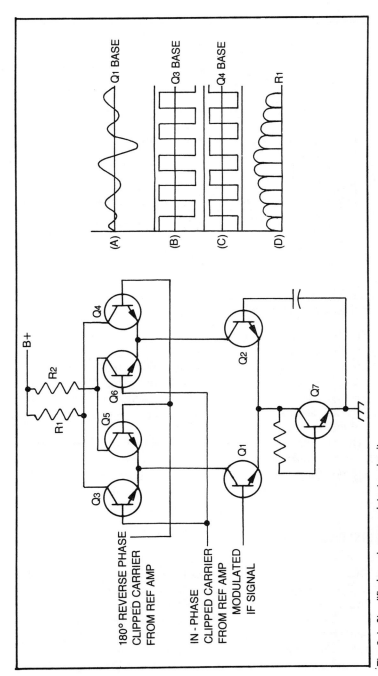

Fig. 6-4. Simplified synchronous detector circuit.

161

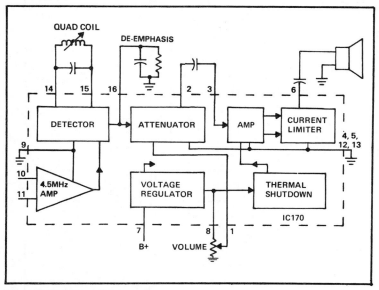

Fig. 6-5. IC 170 audio circuitry.

1. Pin 2 is the output terminal of the attenuator. This output is capacitively coupled to pin 3, the amplifier input. The amplifier output is pin 6, and this is capacitively coupled to the speaker.

The B+ voltage for IC 170 is connected to pin 7, the input of the voltage regulator. The voltage regulator output is connected to the internal circuits and pin 8. This provides a stabilized voltage source for the VOLUME control.

Overdissipation protection is provided by the current limiting and thermal shutdown circuitry. Power dissipation of IC 170 is · largely governed by the impedance of the speaker, which is 32 ohms. A lower impedance speaker would increase power dissipation.

IC 300 Chroma Chip

The chroma integrated circuit, IC 300, contains the band-pass amplifier, burst gate, 3.58-MHz oscillator, color control, color killer, APC (automatic phase control) detector and chroma demodulator functions. Refer to Fig. 6-6 for a block diagram of IC 300.

The band-pass amplifier input is at pin 15. The amplifier output is connected internally to the burst gate. Horizontal keying pulses are fed to the burst gate via pin 13. The burst gate has two outputs. One output is the chroma sideband signal, which is fed internally to the color section. The other is the gated signal that is fed from pin 17 to pin 11, the input of the APC detector. The APC ADJUSTMENT control, R324, is connected to pins 9 and 10. The 3.58-MHz crystal is connected to pins 8 and 6, and a phase-shift network connects pin 7 to pin 6. The oscillator is connected internally to the demodulator and the color killer. The color killer has no external adjustments.

The color control section is DC-controlled and has two control inputs, pins 18 and 20. Pin 18 is permanently connected for maximum gain. Pin 20 is connected to the COLOR control. The output of the COLOR control section will be found at chip pin 19.

This output signal at pin 19 goes via phase-shift networks to the demodulator inputs at pins 2, 3 and 4. The phase-shift networks provide signals of the correct phase and amplitude for the demodulator inputs. Pins 2, 3 and 4 are DC-coupled to a source voltage from pin 5 so that the demodulator DC output voltages will track each other, preventing undesirable gray scale shifts.

The TINT control circuit is connected between the outputs of the burst gate and the input of the APC detector. This is in the path of the gated burst signal. The circuit acts as a tuned RLC network, providing variable delay to the signal.

Because the burst signal controls the phase of the 3.58-MHz oscillator, it changes the phase angle between the 3.58-MHz refer-

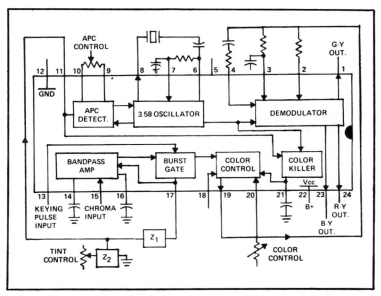

Fig. 6-6. Chroma IC block diagram.

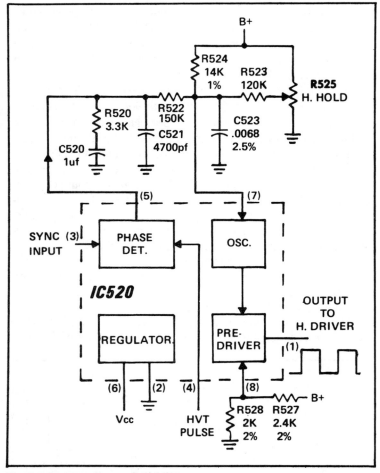

Fig. 6-7. IC 520 horizontal processor.

ence signal and the chroma sideband signal. The variable element in the TINT control impedance network acts as a variable resistance. As the current through it changes, its apparent resistance changes. As a result, the impedance of that leg of the network changes, varying the delay of the color burst signal.

IC 520 Horizontal Processor

Referring to the circuit shown in Fig. 6-7, you will note that IC 520 contains the horizontal phase detector, horizontal oscillator and horizontal predriver. The sync pulse input to the phase detector is pin 3. The horizontal keying pulse enters at pin 4, and the phase detector output is at pin 5. Capacitor C521 with R520 and C520 filter the correction voltage. And R522 couples the phase detector output to the oscillator control input at pin 7.

The oscillator is an RC type with the frequency controlling components connected to pin 7. These components are C523, R523, R524 and R525. The oscillator is connected internally to the predriver.

The predriver converts the oscillator signal into a rectangular wave (pulse) which is fed out of pin 1 to the horizontal driver stage. The duty cycle on this wave is determined by the voltage at pin 8, which is controlled very closely by the 2-percent tolerance resistors, R527 and R528. The IC has an internal regulator which holds the voltage at pin 6 to about 8 volts DC.

Video Signal Troubleshooting

The video signal path in Fig. 6-8 has five divisions that will aid you in troubleshooting. These are as follows:

- From tuner to the output of IC 120 where the signal for the audio circuit comes off.
- From the output of IC 120 to the collector and emitter of Q200 where the signals for the sync and color circuits come off.
- From Q200 to C220 where DC restoration occurs. The BRIGHTNESS control is in this division.

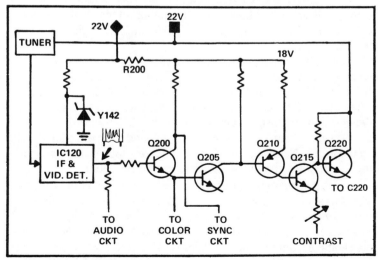

Fig. 6-8. Video amplifier stages.

- From C220 to the video output of the main circuit board. The BRIGHTNESS control is in this division.
- From the output of the main circuit board to the CRT.

These divisions will help you diagnose by symptoms. For example, if the symptom is no video but the audio is good, the trouble is not likely to be between the tuner and IC 120. Or if there is color but no video, the fault would be between Q200 and the CRT. In this case, if the BRIGHTNESS control will adjust the screen brightness, the trouble is between Q200 and Q220. Thus, you can localize the trouble by knowing where the audio, sync and color signals split off from the video signals and noting which signals are missing.

Use a scope for troubleshooting video problems. At pin 12 of IC 120, a normal video signal has negative-going sync pulses and is about 3 volt peak-to-peak. At the emitter of Q200, the sync pulses are the same polarity but they are positive-going at the collector. At C220 and at the output of the main circuit board, they are also positive-going. Use your scope to check for proper polarity and any sign of sync clipping.

Note that there are two DC-coupled sections. One of these is from pin 12 of IC 120 to the emitter of Q220. The other is from the base of Q224 to the CRT cathode. Note that this DC coupling is important because a loss of voltage at any point in the DC-coupled chain will affect the voltage in all of the stages that follow. For example, if something happens to the voltage at pin 12 of IC 120, the voltages on Q200, Q205, Q210, Q215 and Q220 will also be affected.

One other notable characteristic is that there are three voltage sources for the video signal circuits. The tuner, Q215 and Q220 are fed from a 22-volt supply developed from the 60-Hz bridge rectifier. The color-difference amplifiers are fed from a 140-volt supply also developed from the 60-Hz bridge rectifier. IC 120 and Q200 through Q220 are fed from a 22-volt supply developed from the high-voltage transformer. Naturally, all of these voltage supplies must be working in order for the video signal stages to operate.

The last characteristic to be covered does not affect the video signal as such, but it does affect the operation of the color-difference amplifiers. The color-difference circuit is shown in Fig. 6-9. This characteristic is that the color difference amplifiers receive base bias voltage from the chroma chip, IC 300. If the base voltages are incorrect, the screen brightness or the gray scale will be affected.

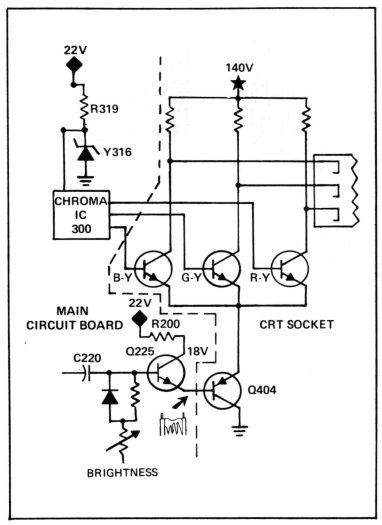

Fig. 6-9. Color-difference amplifier circuit.

ZENITH TRIPLE-PLUS COLOR CHASSIS

In this section we will be looking at the master scan oscillator, some logic circuits and vertical countdown divider circuits used in the Zenith Triple-Plus color chassis. Also, we will see some oscilloscope waveforms and troubleshooting tips for the chroma and low-level luminance ICs found in this TV chassis.

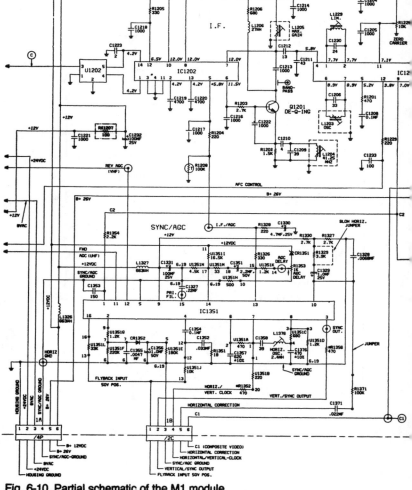

Fig. 6-10. Partial schematic of the M1 module.

Master Scan Oscillator and AGC Operation

For a discussion of these circuits, refer to Fig. 6-10, which is a partial schematic of the M1 module. The agc voltage for the i-f appears at pin 13, and composite sync pulses exit at pin 3. The 503-kHz oscillator clock signal exits at pin 7 of IC 1351.

Referring to the block diagram in Fig. 6-11, let's look at some of the external components associated with the agc-sync of IC 1351. The output of the synchronous detector is fed to pin 1 via a low-pass

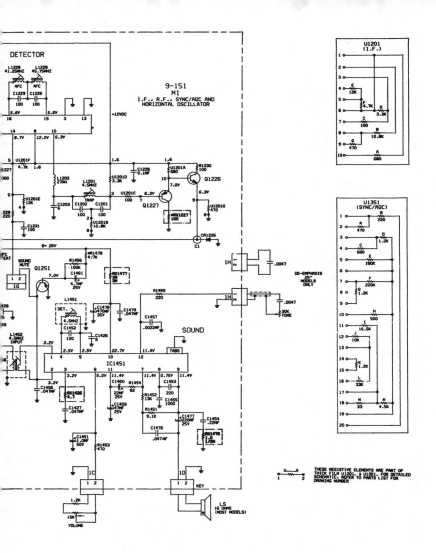

RC network to filter out the 4.5-MHz sound. In the IC, this signal is applied to an agc comparator. The agc comparator samples the sync tip level, compares it to a 4-volt reference level from the agc gate circuit during the gating time, and then either charges, discharges or does nothing to the primary filter capacitor C1327 at pin. The gating time is determined by the time coincidence of the keying pulse coupled to the IC at pin 16 and the sync pulses from the sync separator.

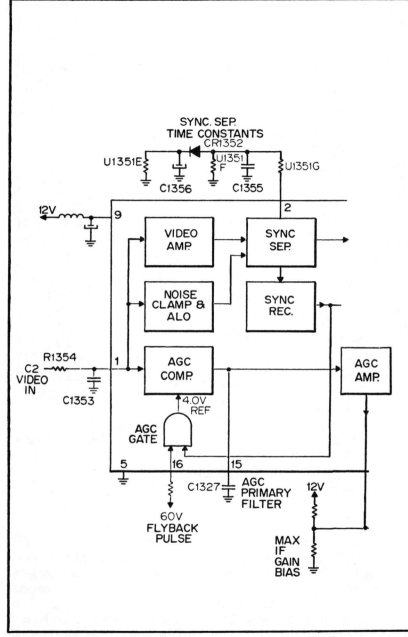

Fig. 6-11. Block diagram of the IC 1351.

170

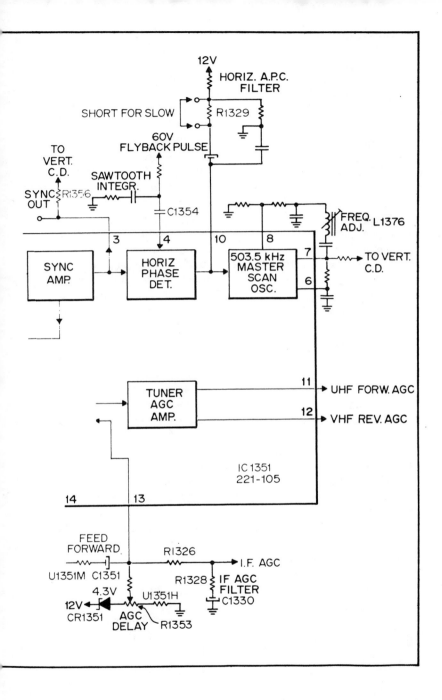

171

The DC level of the primary filter capacitor C1327 is fed to the agc amplifier. The purpose of the internal agc amplifier is to limit the swing of the i-f agc voltage from the maximum i-f gain point to the delay crossover point. This point is determined by the bias at pin 14 and the agc delay setting of R1353 and the DELAY control at pin 13. There is an RC external network between pin 13 and 14, which is called a *feed forward* circuit and allows additional gain reduction beyond the crossover point in the event of large, fast changes in signal strength. The i-f agc output is filtered before it is applied to the i-f. This filter consists of resistors R1326, R1328 and capacitor C1330. Notice the zener diode in series with the AGC DELAY control. This is a 4.3-volt zener diode, and its purpose is to provide for a constant delay or crossover point independent of B+ variations. This entire circuit and others reduce the need for module adjustments or alignment when a faulty module must be replaced.

At pin 11, a forward agc output is provided for the VHF tuner is provided and, at pin 12, reverse agc output is provided for VHF tuner for signal strengths beyond the delay point. Video from the C2 input is fed to a video amplifier within the IC, which in turn applies it to a sync separator. The normal dual-time constant sync separator component network is located at pin 2.

At pin 4, a phase detector is within IC 1351. In addition to receiving the sync pulses, this detector also receives a sawtooth voltage generated by integrating the 60-volt positive flyback pulse by capacitors C1354 and C1352. The phase detector output is filtered at pin 10, and the noise immunity of the master scan oscillator system is determined by the value of components located at pin 10. These component values were selected with video tape viewing in mind that may have excessive skewing errors.

Within the IC, shown in Fig. 6-11, the output from the phase detector is fed to the 503.5-kHz master scan oscillator. It is referred to as a master scan oscillator because its output frequency is not at a vertical rate, nor at the horizontal rate, but at a rate that is 32 times the 15,734-Hz horizontal frequency rate. This output is applied to the countdown IC 2126 on the M2 module which, in turn, counts down the 32 times rate (503 kHz) to the horizontal rate and an additional 262.5 times to the vertical rate. Three pins are used for this internal master scan oscillator (pins 6, 7 and 8) with the output for the vertical and horizontal countdown taken from pin 7. The correct master scan oscillator sinewave signal that should be found at pin 7 is shown in the Fig. 6-12.

The frequency of the master scan oscillator is adjusted by shorting a test stake at pin 3, marked sync out, to ground and

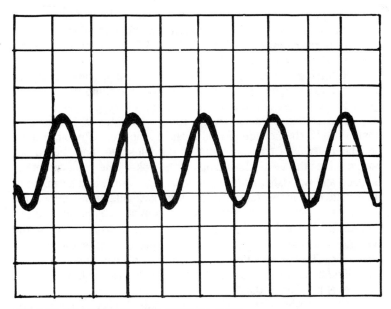

Fig. 6-12. Correct master scan sinewave signal.

adjusting the core of the frequency adjustment coil L1376 for zero beat of the horizontal and vertical by looking at the TV screen to obtain the slowest roll of the picture.

Vertical Countdown System

As you refer to the block diagram in Fig. 6-13, we will discuss various points of the vertical countdown, IC 2126. This is a new Zenith chip and has a 221-103 part number. This chip accepts the 503-kHz signal from the M1 module, composite sync, and operates from 12 volts, 62 volts, and 130 volts. It provides vertical deflection, horizontal drive to the predriver, and a blanking output to the low-level luminance circuits.

As shown on the left side of Fig. 6-14, the vertical system accepts a clock signal from M1 that provides a signal to pin 9 32 times the horizontal frequency (32 H or 503 kHz). The IC divides this by 16 and then 2 (down to H) before feeding the signal into the buffer amplifier to drive the horizontal predriver located on the M3 module. In the bottom left of Fig. 6-13, the flyback pulse is compared to the incoming horizontal sync pulses in an external phase-locked loop, which regulates the 503-kHz oscillator.

The entire vertical sweep, in addition to the IC, consists of two power transistors and other peripheral circuit components. Do not look for or try to adjust the VERTICAL HOLD control because this countdown system does not require one.

Referring back to Fig. 6-14, the logic circuit provides a pulse to trigger a ramp generator. Associated with the ramp generator at pins 2 and 3 is a SIZE control and a ramp-forming capacitor.

The voltage ramp from the ramp generator is DC-coupled inside the IC to one side of a differential amplifier. The differential amplifier drives a transistor power output stage, and the output stage drives the vertical windings of the yoke. The yoke current is sensed and waveshaped in the feedback network, and a sample of that yoke current is coupled to the feedback side of the differential amplifier at pin 5. Therefore, the differential amplifier and output stages function to make the sample of yoke current look just like the voltage ramp at its input. This technique enhances the vertical linearity. The logic section also provides a blanking pulse which is amplified by another buffer stage and coupled through pin 7 to the low-level luminance IC 2226.

The logic circuitry also has other inputs. It receives integrated vertical pulses at pin 12 to make sure that the vertical retrace interval coincides with the vertical interval of composite sync. Also, the logic circuit receives composite sync at pin 13 as it must decide if the incoming signal is standard or nonstandard. If the signal has 525 lines per frame, then the ramp generator is triggered by the countdown chain in the IC, and all of the advantages that come with a countdown result, such as good interlace and good noise immunity. If the signal does not have 525 lines per frame, then the ramp generator is triggered by the integrated vertical pulse which still drives the yoke, but interlace and noise immunity may be affected. Thus, the logic circuit must know if the incoming signal is standard or nonstandard. This logic circuit "looks" at the composite sync signal during the vertical interval for a period of six lines. If the signal is a standard NTSC signal, the composite sync will have proper serrations, and the logic circuit should count 12 pulse edges during the 6-line time period. If the logic period circuit does not count at least nine edges during the 6-line time period, it decides that the signal is non-NTSC or nonstandard and, therefore, does not necessarily have 525 lines.

Sync Signal Examples

Examples of nonstandard signals are those from some cable systems, some pattern generators and various types of closed

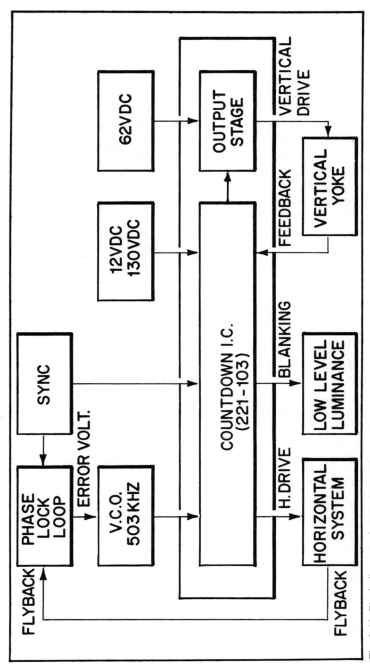

Fig. 6-13. Block diagram of vertical countdown chip.

175

circuit TV camera systems. Examples of standard signals are produced in television station transmitters and quality color-bar generators.

However, not all signals with enough serrations are standard NTSC signals with 525 lines per frame. At times, some signals might exist that can confuse the decision-making process in the logic circuit. Thus, to force the correct response, a mode override jumper is provided at pin 8 of the IC on the M2 board. If this jumper is left plugged in, the logic circuit makes it own decision about whether the signal is standard or nonstandard. If the jumper is disconnected and left open-circuited, the logic is forced into a nonstandard mode. Normally, the jumper should be left plugged in. However in some areas, there just could be a signal where this system will not lock in the picture properly. In this rare instance, the jumper should be disconnected. The circuit should then lock onto the signal, but the advantages of countdown will be lost (interlace and noise immunity).

At pin 1 of the IC, a 5-volt regulator is included. Most of the circuitry inside the IC uses 5 volts, which is generated from 12 volts. The 5 volts, filtered at pin 4 by external circuitry, is used for bias networks at pins 12 and 9.

ZENITH FM STEREO MULTIPLEX CHIP OPERATION

In this Zenith system, the FM rf signal is first processed by the rf and i-f stages before being coupled to the detector stage. The output of the detector stage is coupled to IC 301 in the phase-locked loop circuit. Depending on the type of signal received, the output of IC301 will automatically produce monaural or stereo audio information. Refer to the overall circuit and scope waveforms required for troubleshooting this FM stereo multiplex system in Fig. 6-15.

Ceramic Filters

As you can see in Fig. 6-16, there are only two tunable LC devices in the FM i-f stages. One is the first i-f transformer (T201), and the other is the quadrature coil (L205). Y201 and Y202 are the two ceramic filters used in the FM i-f stages. These ceramic filters reduce the number of tunable circuits required and also simplify alignment.

Being highly selective, ceramic filters provide approximately 75 percent of the i-f selectivity. Ceramic filters are not tunable and fall into various center frequency groups. For this reason, the signal generator must be set to the center frequency of the ceramic filters when i-f stage alignment is performed.

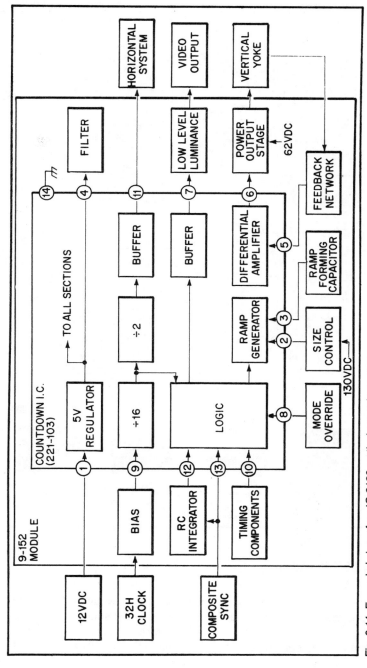

Fig. 6-14. Expanded view of an IC 2126 vertical countdown chip.

177

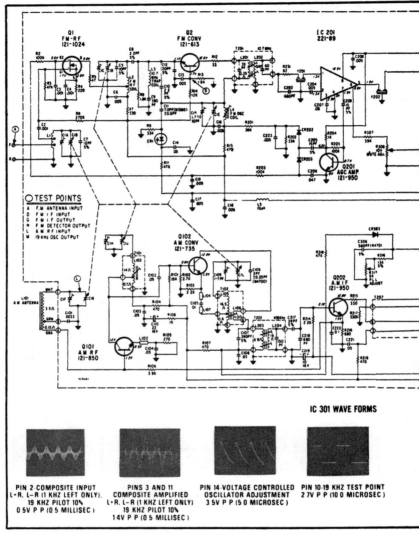

Fig. 6-15. Overall FM stereo circuit.

FM AGC Operation

Again referring to Fig. 6-16, note that agc amplifier Q201, along with the voltage doubler diodes, controls the gain of the FM rf amplifiers. A voltage divider from the FM B+ source forms the initial bias of +5.6 volts at gate 2 of the rf FET. This represents the optimum gain condition for the rf amplifier. FM signals are sampled

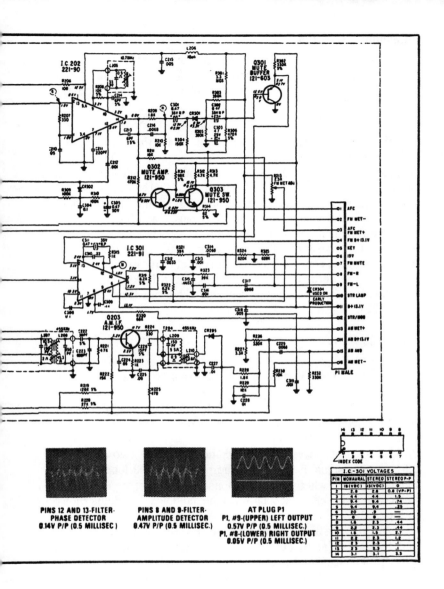

| PINS 12 AND 13-FILTER-PHASE DETECTOR 0.14V P/P (0.5 MILLISEC.) | PINS 8 AND 9-FILTER-AMPLITUDE DETECTOR 0.47V P/P (0.5 MILLISEC.) | AT PLUG P1 P1, #9-(UPPER) LEFT OUTPUT 0.57V P/P (0.5 MILLISEC.) P1, #8-(LOWER) RIGHT OUTPUT 0.05V P/P (0.5 MILLISEC.) |

I.C.-301 VOLTAGES

PIN	MONAURAL	STEREO	STEREO P-P
1	1B (VDC)	13 (VDC)	0
2	2.8	2.8	0.8 (VP-P)
3	4.4	4.4	1.5
4	9.4	9.4	.74
5	9.4	9.4	.85
6	2.0	.9	—
7	0	0	—
8	1.5	2.3	.44
9	2.2	2.3	.44
10	1.5	1.5	2.7
11	2.2	2.3	1.2
12	2.3	2.3	.1
13	2.3	2.3	—
14	3.1	3.1	3.3

at pin 7 of IC 201. They are coupled through C209 to the base of Q201 where the signal is amplified and coupled through C205 to the junction of CR202 and CR203. When the signal reaches sufficient amplitude, diodes CR202 and CR203 conduct, lowering the voltage of gate 2 of the rf FET from +5.6 volts, thus lowering the gain for the rf FET.

FM Multiplex Operation

The FM rf signal is first processed by the rf and i-f stages before being coupled to the detector stage. The output of the detector stage is coupled to IC 301 in the phase-locked loop circuit.

Monaural FM Mode

When a monaural rf signal is selected by the receiver, the output of IC 202 will consist of only audio information. This audio is coupled to pin 2 of IC 301. A block diagram of the phase-lock loop circuitry is provided in Fig. 6-17. The audio signal is processed by a limiter amplifier and coupled to a decoder circuit. The decoder circuit produces equal output signals at pins 4 and 5 of IC 301.

The remaining circuitry located in IC 301 is not used during monaural FM reception. The audio signal after going through the amplifier stage is coupled from pin 3 to pin 11 of IC 301 by capacitor C308. For the detector circuitry to function, a 19-kHz pilot signal must be present. This signal is present only during transmission of stereo FM.

FM Stereo Mode

It is during stereo reception that the phase-locked loop is utilized. When the FM rf tuner is tuned to a stereo station, the FM signal is processed in the rf and i-f stages as with monaural reception. The output of IC 202, the detector stage, during stereo reception contains left plus right audio as well as left minus right (23 kHz to 58 kHz) information that is amplitude-modulated with a 38-kHz surpressed carrier. In addition to these two signals, a 19-kHz pilot signal is present. The phased-locked loop circuitry must determine whether an FM monoural or FM stereo signal has been selected. The block diagram of the multiplex decoder is shown in Fig. 6-18.

Amplitude and Trigger Stage. For the amplitude detector and trigger stage to determine the presence of stereo info, a 19-kHz pilot signal and an in-phase 19-kHz signal generated by the voltage-controlled oscillator must be present simultaneously. If the pilot signal is of sufficient amplitude, a control signal will be processed by the low-pass filter and coupled to the trigger stage. The trigger stage will provide a current source for the stereo indicator lamp and simultaneously activate the stereo switch circuit. The stereo switch circuitry will allow a 38-kHz signal that is in phase with the 19-kHz pilot signal to be coupled to the demodulator.

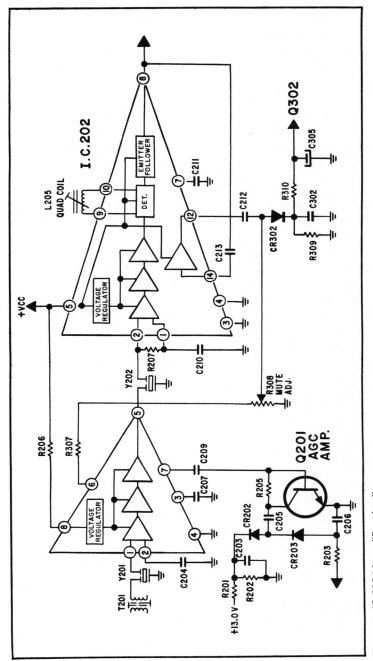

Fig. 6-16. IC 202 i-f amplifier circuits.

181

FM Limiter/Detector. IC 202 is the chip that receives the output from IC 201. IC 202 is the FM limiter/detector chip. A simplified illustration in Fig. 6-16 shows the functions performed within both ICs. Both IC 201 and IC 202 contain three gain/limiter stages and a voltage regulator stage. IC 202 also contains a quadrature detector, an emitter follower and a voltage amplifier.

FM Interstation Muting. Transistor Q301 also mutes the audio channel when the receiver is tuned between FM stations. During this period of time, a noise will be present at pin 8 of IC 202. The noise pulses are coupled through C213 to pin 14 of IC 202. The noise is amplified within IC 202 and appears at pin 12 of the IC. These noise pulses are then coupled through C212 to diode CR302. Diode CR302 detects the amplified noise pulses and develops a positive DC voltage that is present at the base of transistor Q302. This causes Q302 to conduct. The resultant drop in collector voltage is coupled to the base of transistor Q303. This will cause Q303 to switch off. The collector voltage at Q303 will switch towards B+. The higher positive voltage is coupled through resistors R313 and R304 to the cathode of diode CR301, turning the diode off. Thus, the signal path to transistor Q301 is opened, preventing the noise pulses from being coupled to the audio output stages.

The FM AFC Mode. The DC output at pin 8 of IC 202 is also used to provide afc action for the local oscillator in the converter stage. The DC potential at pin 8 is coupled via R212 and R11 to the cathode of varactor diode CR1. The capacitance value of CR1 is inversely proportional to the voltage applied across the diode. CR1 is connected to the local oscillator circuit in the converter stage. As the voltage across the diode increases, the capacity of the diode increases. This causes an increase in the frequency of the local oscillator. Just the opposite is true if the voltage across the diode decreases. The capacity will increase, causing a decrease in the local oscillator frequency.

If a strong station is adjacent to a weak station, the ability to tune in the weak station may be prevented by the afc action. To let you tune in a weak station, an AFC DEFEAT switch is provided on the front panel of the receiver. With the AFC switch in the off position, a fixed DC voltage is fed to the afc line from B+.

Pilot Signal Regeneration

A voltage-controlled oscillator (VCO) is used to obtain both the 19-kHz and 38-kHz signals necessary to allow stereo reception to take place. The 19-kHz pilot signal present at pin 11 of IC 301 is fed

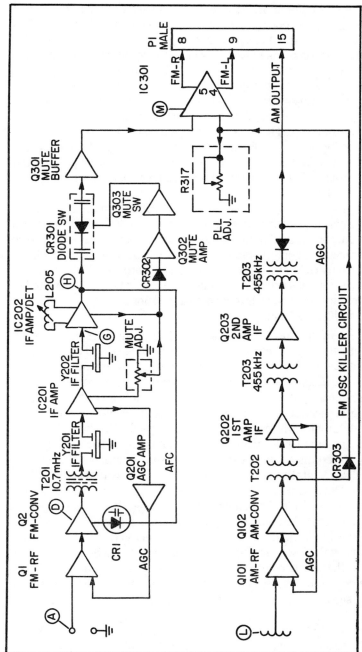

Fig. 6-17. Block diagram of phase-locked loop circuitry.

183

to the phase detector. Also fed to the phase detector is a second 19-kHz signal generated by the VCO. The VCO is designed to operate at 76 kHz. A divide by two stage is used to develop a 38-kHz signal that will be used to demodulate the left minus right information. A second divide by two stage is used to produce the 19-kHz signal that is coupled back to the phase detector. The phase detector will develop an error signal that is proportional to the frequency and phase differences of the two 19-kHz signals. This error signal is used to develop a DC correction voltage that is fed to the VCO. The correction voltage will cause the VCO to change frequency and phase until the resultant 19-kHz signal is identical to the phase of the pilot signals. The original 19-kHz pilot signal is identical to the phase of the pilot signal.

Also, the original 19-kHz pilot signal was in phase with the suppressed 38-kHz carrier. The regenerated 38-kHz carrier signal can now be coupled to the demodulator circuitry to be added to the left minus right information. When this has been accomplished, the left minus right audio information can be detected. The two audio signals, left plus right and left minus right, are then demodulated to reproduce left and right channel information.

Analog IC Chip Testing

An IC checker for general consumer product troubleshooting is not yet practical, and the cost would be too great. The next best technique for the technician to troubleshoot these chips is to consider the IC as a black box. For this testing concept, you must know what signal input to expect and what the output should be. Thus, by using an oscilloscope for measuring the input and output signals, you can determine whether or not the IC is good. This black box chip testing method is illustrated in Fig. 6-19 as it could be applied to an FM stereo multiplex decoder IC package. For these checks you need a FM stereo generator and a high-gain, wide-band oscilloscope. The first step would be to make sure all DC voltages to the IC are correct. Then check for proper composite FM stereo signal at pin 3 of the IC 301 with the scope. All other active pins on the chip can now be checked with the scope for expected waveforms that are shown at the bottom of Fig. 6-19. This same technique can be used to check the in and out of ICs used in i-f amplifiers, audio amplifiers, FM detectors, chroma amplifiers and demodulators. The presence of a signal may also be checked with a VTVM by using a diode detector probe for rf signals.

With this signal tracing concept for testing ICs, you must know what output to expect for a given amount of signal input. When

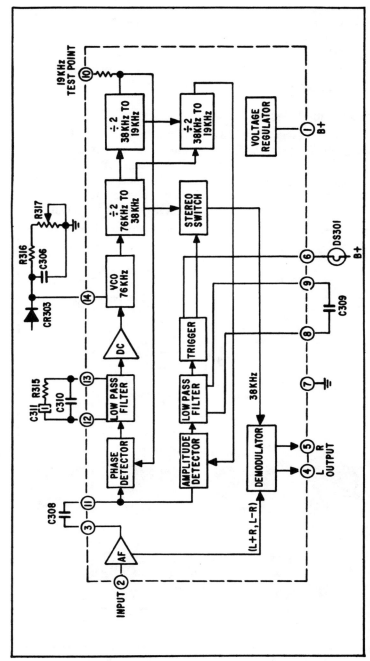

Fig. 6-18. Block diagram of a multiplex decoder.

185

checking an i-f or audio IC amplifier you not only need to know the gain and any control bias data of the chip, but also the frequency range of the input signal for the expected gain. In many cases, this information can be found in the service information data usually supplied by the manufacturer.

Tuned Circuit IC Testing

In some cases, you may want to check the rf signal path through an IC with tuned signal input and output transformer stages. Signal injection may be required so as not to disturb the tuned circuits. Inductive coupling can be used to inject the test signal and to measure the output. A test probe can be fashioned by winding a coil on one end of a small ferrite rod. Or you can use a

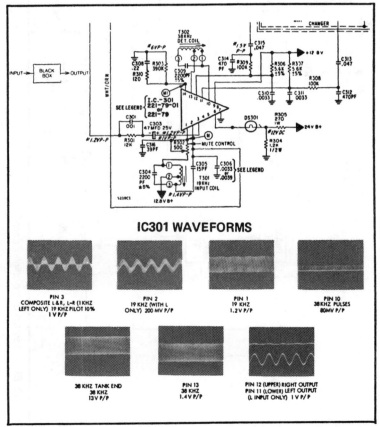

Fig. 6-19. Stereo multiplex decoder IC schematic and black box chip testing.

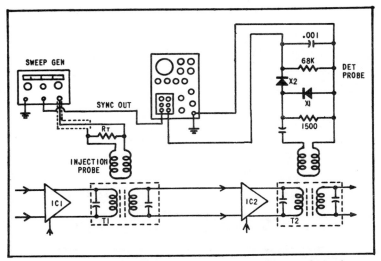

Fig. 6-20. Signal generator and scope test setup for inductive IC checks.

discarded radio or video i-f coil. For circuits that use unshielded coils, slip an air-core coil over the tuned coil under test, which causes less detuning than a ferrite-core coil. The scope probe is connected to the output of the circuit with the same type of coil, thus achieving complete instrument inductive coupling.

The generator should be terminated with the correct resistance across the input coil. Some generators may have the proper termination built into the cable leads. Shunt the pick-up coil with a 1500-ohm termination resistor and connect the scopes rf detector probe across it. Figure 6-20 shows the complete test setup.

CAUTION NOTE: Always use the minimum amount of generator signal that will provide an output indication on the scope. For best results use minimum generator output and more vertical scope gain while maintaining very loose coupling. Check alignment after any fault has been found and corrected. For a resonance check of a single unshielded coil, it's best to use a grid-dip or tunnel-dipper meter.

To recap IC troubleshooting, remember there is no practical IC checker that you can now use. Thus, you should verify that the supply voltages (V_{cc}) are correct and that the DC voltages at the pins of the IC are within tolerance. If correct input signal is then present but other symptoms and output scope waveforms indicate a faulty IC, then substitute a known good chip and recheck the operation of the set.

Chapter 7
TV Electronic Tuning Systems

We begin this chapter with a look at the basic phase-locked loop (PPL) circuits. Then comes some additional information on (PLL) and voltage-controlled oscillators (VCO).

Information and problem checkouts for one of RCA's direct address remote control tuning systems will be the next item covered. The last section will cover the General Electric remote/ electronic tuning system that uses infrared signals for control. We will be looking at decoder operation, DC voltage-controlled varactor tuning for electronic tuners and much more.

BASIC PHASE-LOCKED LOOP

The basic phase-locked loop has three components:
- A voltage-controlled oscillator (VCO).
- A phase detector.
- A low-pass filter.

Note the basic PLL block diagram in Fig. 7-1.

The phase detector compares the phase of an input signal with the phase of the VCO. Thus the phase detector measures the phase difference of these two input signals. This difference voltage is then filtered and fed into the VCO. The VCO control voltage adjusts the frequency in order to reduce the phase difference between the input signal and oscillator. When the loop is locked in, the control voltage keeps the VCO frequency on the exact average frequency of the input signal. For each cycle of the input signal, there is only one cycle of the oscillator output. Phase-locked loop control is currently

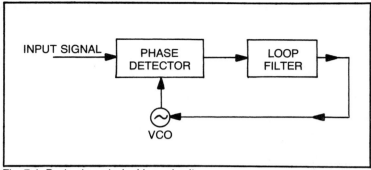
Fig. 7-1. Basic phase-locked loop circuit.

used for automatic frequency control (afc) in many electronic equipment applications. With the phase-locked loop technique, exact frequency control can be achieved, while conventional afc circuits have some frequency error.

Most phase-locked loops produce a small amount of control voltage (not zero volts) from the output of the phase detector to maintain lock-in. Thus, the loop operates with some phase error present. In a well designed PLL, this error voltage will be quite small.

If the incoming signal is modulated by phase or frequency, some noise will usually be present. Thus the phase-locked system must reproduce the original signal while filtering out as much noise as possible.

In radio receivers, the local oscillator signal, which is very close to the expected signal, is used for the feedback control. The local oscillator and incoming signal waveform are compared with one another by a phase detector whose error output indicates the phase difference. To suppress noise, the error is averaged over a period of time, and this averaged error is used to control the oscillator frequency.

If the signal is stable, the local oscillator will require very little information to track, and this information can be averaged over a long time period, thus eliminating large noise levels. The input to the loop is usually a noisy signal while the output of the VCO is a cleaned-up version of the input signal. Two things to note about the filter is that the bandwidth can be narrowed and the filter automatically tracks the signal frequency. A narrow bandwidth is capable of rejecting large amounts of noise. These features—automatic tracking and narrow bandwidth—account for most applications of phase-locked loops in receivers.

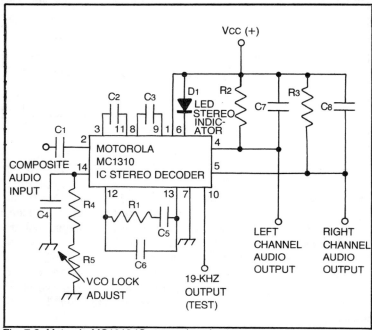

Fig. 7-2. Motorola MC1310 IC stereo decoder (courtesy of Motorola).

MOTOROLA IC STEREO DECODER

AM FM stereo decoder is represented by the Motorola MC130 integrated circuit shown in Fig. 7-2. This is the so-called coiless FM stereo decoder that has seen applications in many consumer electronic products. This same chip will also be found in some modern FM stereo auto radio receivers.

In both types of stereo decoders, you will notice alignment instructions that make use of Lissajous patterns on an oscilloscope to check for the exact 38-kHz frequency. I have found that these checks can be bypassed and you can make use of the capture and lock-in features of the PLL to make these adjustments. The stereo indicator lamp is used to tell us when lock-in occurs.

Oscillator Frequency Adjustment Tips

Adjust the oscillator frequency control until the stereo indicator lamp comes on and stays lighted. Then adjust the main tuning dial of the radio up and down the FM band making sure that the lamp comes on every time a stereo FM station is received. Be sure to check several stations as you tune from above or below the station.

ADDITIONAL PHASE-LOCKED LOOP REVIEW

A basic frequency synthesis (FS) is shown in Fig. 7-3 of the phase-locked loop block diagram. This basic system utilizes the phase-locked loop (PLL) principle in conjunction with a digital frequency programmer to generate a number of discrete frequencies.

Phase-locked loops have been used in a number of electronic applications over the past few years. Some uses include FM stereo decoding, demodulation of FM signals, CB radios, VCRs and TV and FM receiver tuners.

Phase locking is actually a technique of forcing the phase of an oscillator signal to exactly follow the phase of a reference signal. The PLL automatically locks onto and tracks a signal, even though its frequency changes. The PLL does all this with the help of its phase comparator and a voltage-controlled oscillator (VCO). Specifically, the phase comparator samples the frequency of an input signal with that of a reference oscillator and produces an error voltage directly in proportion to the difference between the two. For simplicity, you can assume a close relationship between frequency and phase.

The error voltage has two functions. It is fed back to the VCO and changes its frequency to match that of the input signal. This feedback enables the PLL to lock onto and track the signal. The error voltage can also be considered a demodulated FM output since it varies directly with a shift in the input signal frequency. Simply stated, the error voltage from the phase comparator permits the PLL to lock onto a frequency, and to track it continually over a given range.

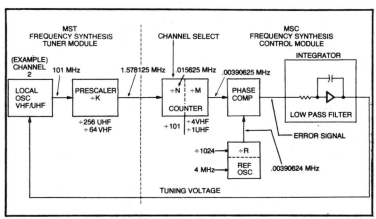

Fig. 7-3. Basic phase-locked loop operation.

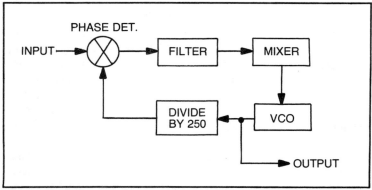

Fig. 7-4. Block diagram of a programmable divider.

CHECKING PLL AND VCO CIRCUITS

The frequency counter is very useful for troubleshooting phase-locked loop circuits. Because these circuits are in a loop configuration, you cannot break the loop for testing purposes and still retain normal operation. Let's consider an actual PLL circuit, the one shown in Fig. 7-4. The problem in this circuit was a wrong frequency out of the VCO.

The programmable divider was set to divide by 250, so the VCO output should have been 17.5 MHz (1 kHz X 250 X 10) + 15 MHz. However, the VCO was locked in at 17.4 MHz. Now to solve this loop problem.

A check with the counter and with the VCO locked in indicates that the VCO, phase detector and filter are operating. But with the wrong frequency out of the VCO, chances are that the fault is in the counter string or mixer, so we just move down the string. A check of the mixer shows us an output of 2.4 MHz, which is correct for the mixer output difference between 17.4 MHz and 15 MHz inputs. Now, we know that the input to the first divide-by-10 stage is 2.4 MHz. A look at its output shows it to be 240 kHz, and a correct division by 10, so the input to the programmable divider is 240 kHz. Now a check of the programmable divider output shows exactly 1 kHz. This means the programmable divider is only dividing by 240 instead of 250.

A recheck of the programmable pins on the LSI chip confirms that it was programmed to divide by 250, but was only dividing by 240. The LSI chip was replaced and the problem was solved.

The above example trouble shows that a good stable frequency counter is now required to troubleshoot these modern digital PLL circuits. Note the Sencore counter setup in Fig. 7-5, one that can be used for PLL checks.

A counter can also be used as a check of phase-locked loop circuits to determine how stable the circuit is and in working to improve stability. The range of flashing of the least significant digits gives a good approximation of circuit stability. The counter is a must in servicing to ensure that design criteria and tolerance have been met.

The counter is also useful in checking instruments or equipment with LC or crystal-controlled oscillators. Crystal oscillators have to be checked for tolerance during alignment or servicing, and using a counter is the best way this can be accomplished.

RCA DIRECT ADDRESS TUNING SYSTEM

As we check out some problems that may occur in this RCA direct address remote system, refer to the PC board layout of the remote control module in Fig. 7-6. Some of these RCA remote control trouble symptoms are as follows:

- No or improper channel up/down action.
- No or improper add or erase of the scan memory.
- No or improper channel change or skip.

Preliminary Checks

Check all interface connections and wiring to and from the MSC control module. Each time a channel change is performed,

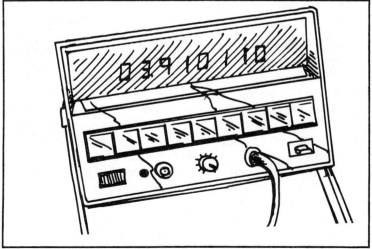

Fig. 7-5. Sencore model FC51 frequency counter used to check a PLL circuit.

note the display readout. This visual readout indication can be used as an aid for tracking down a particular problem.

No or Improper Channel Up/Down Action

Scan up and down channel data requires that the frequency synthesizer chip (U1) receive proper logic conditions to pins 16 and 17 from the SCAN CHANNEL switch. First, confirm good ground connections at terminal S on the MSC 002 module and to the UP/DOWN switch assembly. If the ground is open, scan capability is lost. If either up or down action is lost, check the terminal on the MSC 002 module for a logic low condition when the CONTROL button is pressed.

No or Improper Add or Erase of Scan Memory

Confirm proper logic conditions at terminals T and U on the MSC 002 control module. Make sure the SELECT-LOCK switch is in the select position and that there is a good ground connection at terminal S or the MSC 002 board. An appropriate add or erase line must go to logic low condition to indicate an add or erase function to the scan memory IC (U4). When add or erase functions are not activated, add and erase lines should be idle at logic high (+5 volts DC).

No or Improper Channel Change or Skip

These problems are usually associated with the MSC module. Replace control module MSC 002.

FS SCAN REMOTE SERVICE PROCEDURES

The FS scan remote system utilizes a frequency synthesizer chip U2, memory chip U4, and on-screen channel display/clock chip U3. These ICs and associated components make up the MSC 003 tuner control module for the scan remote system shown in the Fig. 7-7 schematic. With this system, we will focus in on the display/clock interface and remote control servicing procedures.

The scan remote system includes the MCR 003 remote receiver, which also has the remote decoder IC. This IC processes channel up/down, set on/off, and volume up/down information from the remote control unit (CRK 26) via the preamp (MCY 003), and sends appropriate voltage to the MCS 003 control module. The remote receiver also processes function commands from the manual pushbuttons on the set. Also located on the remote receiver is a

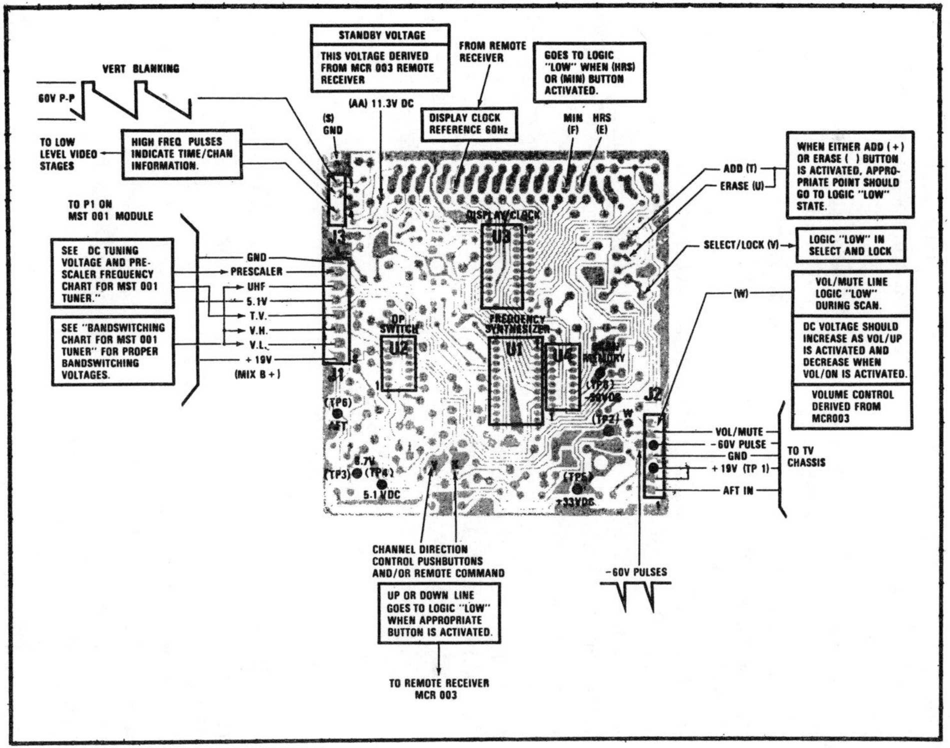

Fig. 7-6. RCA MCS remote control module (courtesy of RCA).

+11 volt DC regulator (Q1101), which provides DC voltages to the remote receiver and preamp board (as long as the TV receiver has AC power connected).

A separate power supply transformer (T1) provides AC power (12 volts) to the regulator Q1101 for standby and operation voltage to the remote receiver and preamp. Relay K1 provides on-off AC power to the receiver.

Symptoms and Service Procedures

Use an isolation transformer and disconnect the line cord during all static checks. Use insulated clipleads for dynamic checks. Check all interface connections and wiring to and from the MSC 003 control module, remote receiver MCR 003 control module, remote receiver MCR 003, preamp MCY 003 and other assemblies within the system.

Unable to Set Time, Erratic Display, or Loss of Time Display. Display problems can be defined as a loss of, erratic, or distorted on-screen digit display with otherwise normal operation. Such problems are usually confined to the clock and display IC (U2503) located on the MSC 003 control module or to connector problems. If problems described above are encountered, replace the MSC 003 module. A defective display assembly may also cause instrument video problems. If video problems are suspected as being caused by the display system, remove connector P3-MSC and see if the problem clears up.

Failure of the system to maintain the correct time of day will usually not occur without the other symptoms being evident. Check the following if this occurs:

- Note any possible intermittent power interruptions. If power to the set is interrupted, the time displayed will be lost when power is restored, requiring the clock to be reset.
- Check the TIME-SET switches and cabling for possible intermittent connections.

No Channel-Up/Down. Check the connections between the remote receiver and preamp. Monitor the logic condition at pins 9 and 11 of U1101 on the remote receiver module. These should go low when the CHANNEL button is depressed. If the logic condition does not change, the problem may be a defective component or remote receiver board. Check for +11 volts DC to the IC (U1101) and preamp board MCY 003.

If the MSC responds to remote control channel up/down, but does not respond to manual channel up/down, check the connec-

196

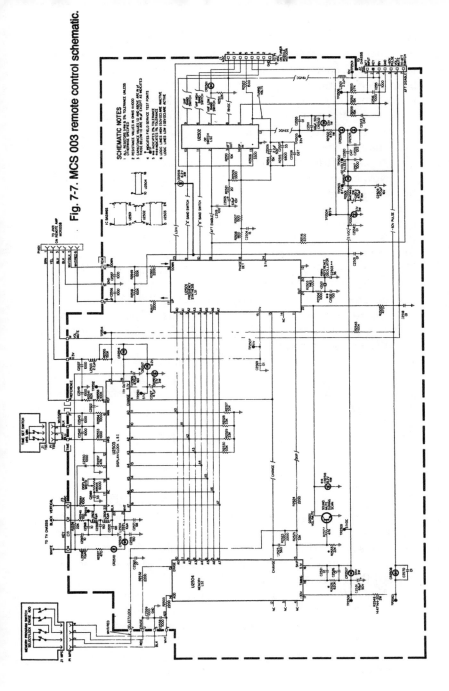

Fig. 7-7. MCS 003 remote control schematic.

197

tions between the remote receiver and the manual button assembly. Check the logic conditions at X and Y on the MSC 003 control module. If proper logic conditions are not present on the MSC board, replace the MCR 00. remote receiver. If the correct logic levels are found on the MSC 003 and you do not get the correct command function, replace the MSC 003 control module.

No or Improper Volume Up/Down. Check for good connections at the remote receiver and preamp. If the connections are OK, replace MCR 003 remote receiver.

Now check for proper connections at J1101 and P1101. If the problem still exists, replace the MCR 003 remote receiver. No or improper volume up/down in remote or manual operation usually indicates a problem associated with the remote decoder IC (U1101), or a problem associated within the TV sound section. First, monitor the DC voltage at point W on the MSC 003 module. Now push the VOLUME UP/DOWN buttons and confirm that the DC voltage tracks when the appropriate button is pressed. If the voltage does not change, replace the MCR 003 modules.

No Remote Control Action (Manual Operation OK). This type problem usually indicates a fault in the CRK-26 transmitter MYC 003 preamp or the MCR 003 remote receiver unit. Check the battery in the remote hand unit. Test for proper mode frequencies of the hand remote unit by connecting the frequency counter to J1103-4 on the MCR 003 remote receiver. The frequencies should be as follows:

Volume up—42.15 kHz.
Volume down—40.55 kHz.
Channel up—39.10 kHz.
Channel down—37.70 kHz.

This also confirms that the preamp (MCY 003) is working properly.

Confirm the presence of +11 volts DC on the MCR 003 module. If the manual tuning operation works properly, the remote decoder IC is receiving +11 volts. A good place to check the +11 volts is at point AA on the MSC module. If all of these check out replace the MCR 003 module.

No On/Off Action From Either Remote or Manual Buttons. On/off problems are usually confined to faults on the MCR 003 remote module. AC power for the TV is via a switching relay circuit, which is also located on this remote module.

Listen for the on/off relay K1 click. This will indicate if the control winding is receiving the DC control voltage for proper on/off

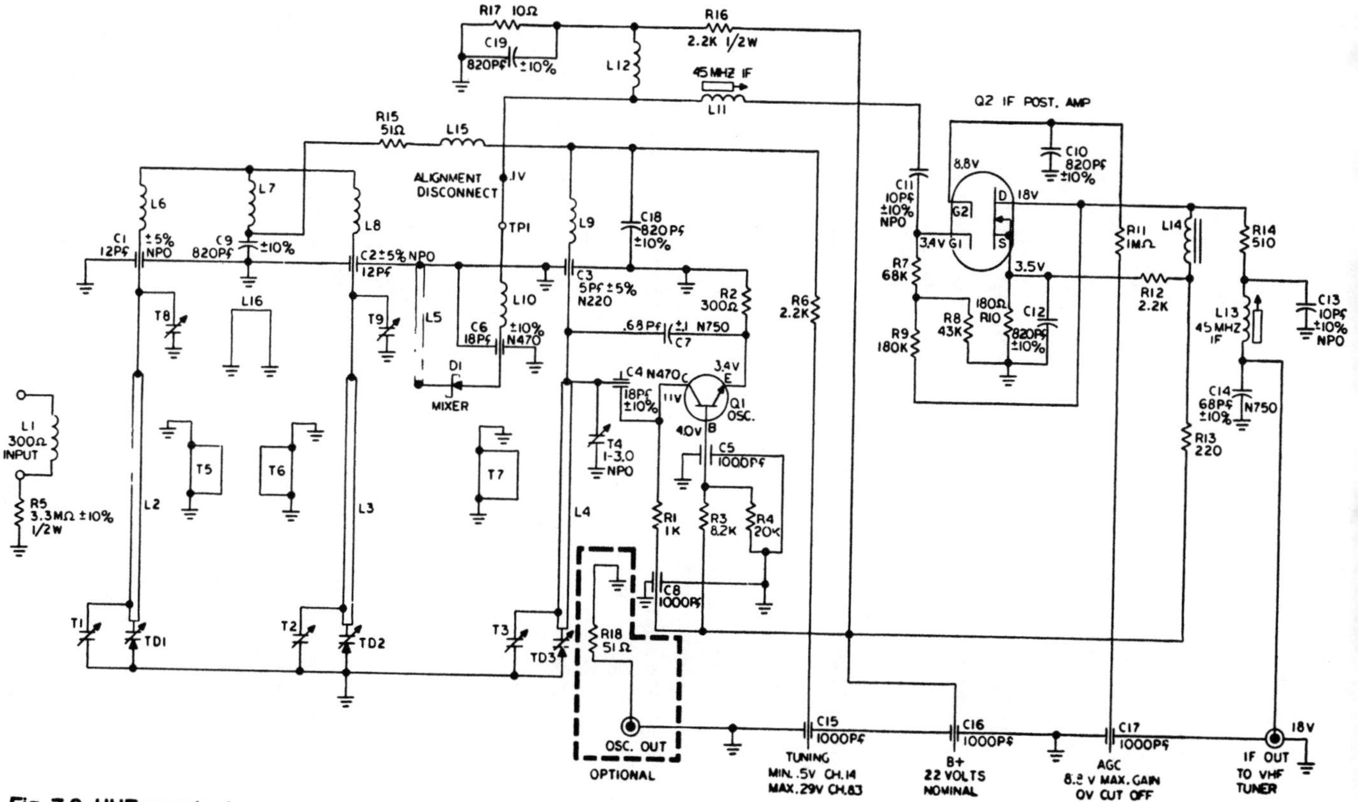

Fig. 7-8. UHF varactor tuner.

199

operation and probably the remote receiver is good. If the relay does not click, check the DC voltage at TS-1101-1 on the remote receiver. If the voltage here tracks up and down as volume up and down is activated, the problem is in relay K1. Voltage at TS 1101-1 should be approximately 1.5 volts minimum for proper ON operation with no volume. If the voltage tracks at TS 1101-1 and the set does not come on, jump pin 1 to 2 of plug P1 on the MCR to restore AC power to the receiver. This step bypasses the MCR 003 remote circuit.

GENERAL ELECTRIC REMOTE/ELECTRONIC TUNING SYSTEM

This GE system uses some of the most recent advances in digital electronics and microcircuitry plus selection of all 82 TV channels. The remote control operates via pulsed a invisible light beam (infrared) signals. This makes the system immune to some types of false triggering which might occur with uncoded ultrasonic systems.

The many TV electronic tuning systems in use today are similar in many respects. All, for example, depend on the varactor tuner for actual channel selection, and all use electronic circuitry to control the varactor tuner. Electronic tuning systems, however, vary widely in technology, principles of operation and complexity. The GE electronic tuning system has modular units and incorporates plugs and connectors to make troubleshooting easier.

In this system, channel selection is precise to the degree of not requiring any FINE TUNING control. The channel selection is simplified as the system acts only on the last two channel digits entered. Multiple channel number entries are ignored, except for the last two digits.

The block diagrams in Figs. 7-8 and 7-9 show the overall GE electronic tuning system. The block diagrams show the inputs, outputs and B+ points for the various components in the system. Even though highly complex electronic processes take place within the modules, their outputs are mainly in the form of DC voltages. For this reason, much of the troubleshooting can be performed with a volt-ohm meter.

The remote receiver module detects the infrared signals from the hand control unit, amplifies them and connects them to the remote decoder module. The remote decoder module also receives inputs from the front panel ON/OFF/VOLUME control assembly. The remote decoder module decodes the commands from the remote receiver and on the ON/OFF/VOLUME controls and translates them into voltages and logic states.

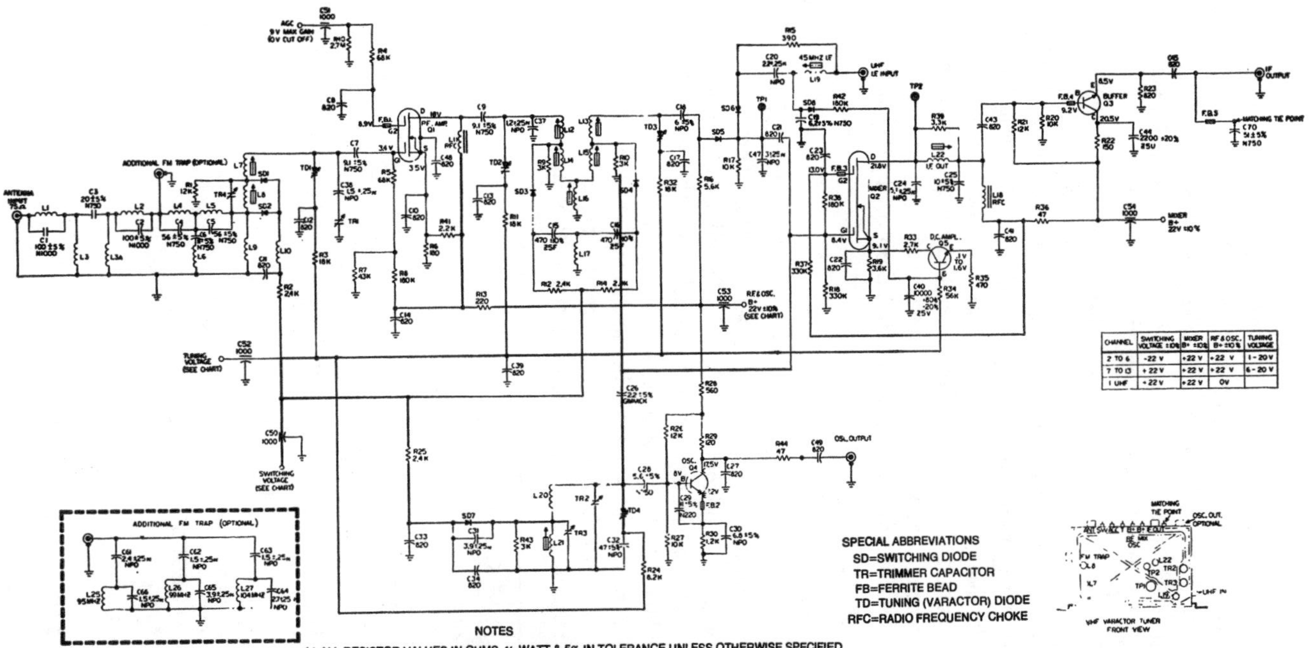

NOTES

1) ALL RESISTOR VALUES IN OHMS, ½ WATT & 5% IN TOLERANCE UNLESS OTHERWISE SPECIFIED
2) ALL CAPACITOR VALUES ARE IN PICOFARADS WITH TOLERANCE & TC AS SPECIFIED ON DWG.
   THE 820pf CAPACITORS ARE ±10% & 25F TYPES.
3) VARACTORS (TD-1 THRU TD-4) ARE MATCHED PER 236145-1.
4) FB1, FB2 & FB3 ARE FERRITE BEADS PER 73A100272-2.
5) FB4 IS FERRITE BEAD PER 73A100272-5.
6) ALL FEED THRUS ARE 1000 pf ±100% ... C.
7) VOLTAGES MAY BE DIFFERENT CHASSIS DESIGNS, SEE THE SCHEMATIC DIAGRAM OF THE
   APPLICABLE CHASSIS FOR THE APPLICABLE VOLTAGES.
8) FOR ALL VOLTAGE MEASUREMENTS USE A HIGH IMPEDANCE (10MΩ OR MORE) METER

SPECIAL ABBREVIATIONS
SD=SWITCHING DIODE
TR=TRIMMER CAPACITOR
FB=FERRITE BEAD
TD=TUNING (VARACTOR) DIODE
RFC=RADIO FREQUENCY CHOKE

CHANNEL	SWITCHING VOLTAGE	MIXER	RF OSC. VOLTAGE	TUNING VOLTAGE
2 TO 6	-22 V	+22 V	+22 V	1 - 20 V
7 TO 13	0 V	+22 V	+22 V	1 - 20 V
1 UHF	0 V	+22 V	+22 V	0V

Fig. 7-9. VHF varactor tuner.

201

The remote decoder module outputs are as follows:

- A DC voltage that activates the on/off function of the TV.
- A DC voltage that controls volume level.
- Various logic states that initiate channel selection.

A +5 volt source is used in the tuner control module to power the circuitry that remembers the received channel before the set was turned off. The tuner control module provides DC controlling voltages to the UHF and VHF tuners and is connected in a closed loop configuration with the tuners. It samples the local oscillator frequencies from the tuners and develops the DC voltages required for channel selection. This unit also provides the logic to program the channel selection. This unit also provides the logic to program the channel number readouts. The electronic tuning system also contains an ON/OFF module that controls AC power to the main power supply of the TV.

Electronic Tuners

The VHF and UHF tuners utilize varactor diodes to perform the frequency changes necessary for channel selection. The varactor diode is a semi-conductor that can be used as a variable capacitor. The change in capacitance exhibited by the varactor diode is caused by the effects of reverse biasing the device with a DC voltage. Figure 7-10 illustrates this capacitance change effect.

When reverse bias is applied to the varactor diode, its charge carriers are attracted away from their normal P-N junction. A

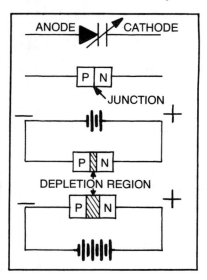

Fig. 7-10. Varactor capacitance change effect.

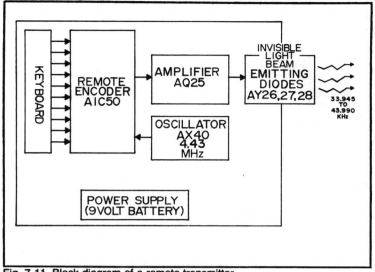

Fig. 7-11. Block diagram of a remote transmitter.

DEPLETION REGION develops in place of the P-N junction, forming—in effect—a dielectric. The P and N material of the varactor diode serve as capacitor plates. With a small amount of reverse bias applied, capacitance is large, because the dielectric (depletion region) is thin. As more reverse bias voltage is applied, capacitance decreases because the depletion region and, hence, the thickness of the dielectric is increased. You may recall that capacitance is inversely proportional to the thickness of the dielectric.

The varactor diodes in the tuners are combined with inductance to form tuned circuits. Thus, with varactor diodes, the tuned circuits in the tuners are voltage controlled. Changes in the DC tuning voltage fed to the tuners thus change the frequency that the tuners select.

Remote Transmitter

The remote transmitter, shown in Fig. 7-11, produces frequency-coded infrared signals. The hand unit keyboard is connected directly to the inputs of the dedicated IC, AIC50, which is the remote encoder. The remote encoder IC produces a different frequency for each remote function. These frequencies, in the range of 33.945 to 43.990 kHz, are amplified and used to modulate infrared light-emitting diodes. A crystal-controlled oscillator provides the frequency reference for the AIC50.

203

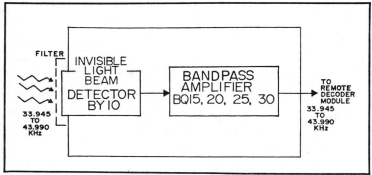

Fig. 7-12. Block diagram of a remote receiver.

Remote Receiver Module

In the remote receiver, shown in Fig. 7-12, a light-sensitive diode is used to detect the infrared beam. Before reaching the diode, the beam first passes through a filter that eliminates virtually all visible light and passes most of the infrared signal. After detection, the pulse-coded information is amplified by a bandpass amplifier and then connected, via a shielded cable, to the remote decoder module.

Remote Decoder Operation

The remote decoder module, shown in Fig. 7-13, controls multiple receiver functions. This module first decodes the amplified intelligence that originated in the remote transmitter. From this and the other inputs, it provides the voltages and logic states needed to control the on/off, volume, and remote channel selection processes of the receiver.

The frequencies received from the receiver module are first processed through a bandpass amplifier and then fed to the input of a specialized IC, DIC50, the remote decoder. The remote decoder IC is referenced to a crystal-controlled oscillator. The oscillator provides the decoder with the same frequency reference as its matching counterpart, the encoder chip in the remote transmitter. The remote decoder translates the frequencies received at its input into output voltages and logic states.

For channel selection logic, all frequencies related to transmitted commands are received by the remote decoder at its input. They exit the chip in the form of 4-bit binary logic. Some of the output pins carry logic information used for the input pins. This is not uncommon in microcircuitry design, as there is a need to limit

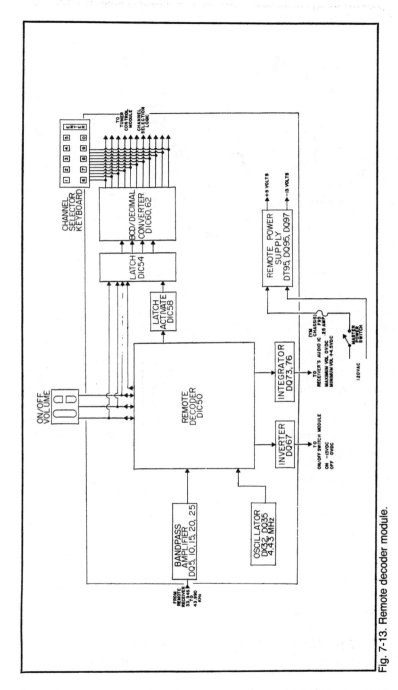

Fig. 7-13. Remote decoder module.

205

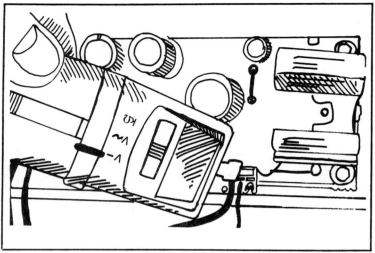

Fig. 7-14. Hobbyist adjusting 5V supply with a digital voltmeter.

the number of pins on complex logic chips. The remote decoder IC differentiates on/off/volume commands and channel selection commands by using an extra bit of logic to identify channel number logic. The extra bit activates DIC58, which allows the remaining channel number processing circuitry to identify the binary logic as a received channel number. When on/off/volume commands appear on the input/output pins, the extra bit is not present and the processing circuitry ignores the command, thus preventing its misinterpretation as channel number logic. The remaining circuitry of the remote decoder, DIC54, 60 and 62, converts the multiple pulsed binary channel number logic into single pulsed decimal logic.

Power Supply Information

The power supply module develops its voltages from an external transformer and diode rectifiers. Two of the sources, +5 and +6.8 volts, are regulated. Figure 7-14 shows a hobbyist adjusting the +5 volt supply with a DVM. Also, a +22 volt source required by the electronic tuning system is obtained from the main TV chassis power supply.

Tuner Control Module

The tuner control module accepts channel selection logic inputs from the keyboard of the TV and the remote decoder module. The primary outputs are DC voltages that activate either the UHF

206

or VHF tuners that switch between VHF high and low bands, and perform channel selection in the tuners. The heart of the tuner control module is the frequency synthesizer chip. A block diagram of the NC6410 IC is shown in Fig. 7-15.

The phase-locked loop, block diagrammed in Fig. 7-16, consists of three stages. These are a highly stable crystal-controlled

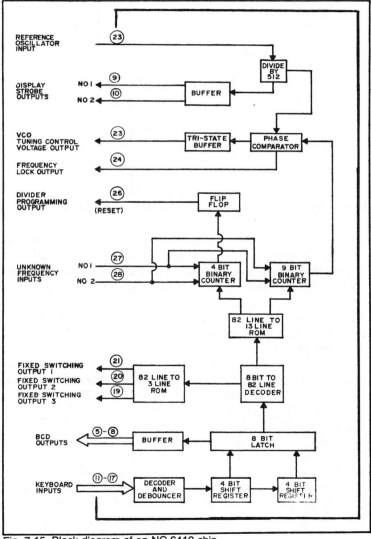

Fig. 7-15. Block diagram of an NC 6410 chip.

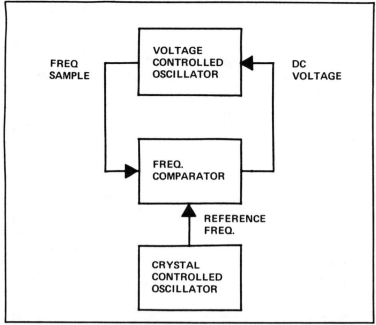

Fig. 7-16. Basic phase-locked loop circuit.

oscillator, a frequency comparator and a voltage-controlled oscillator. The frequency comparator accepts two inputs, the reference sample from the voltage-controlled oscillator and a frequency sample from the voltage-controlled oscillator. It produces one output, a DC voltage that controls the frequency of the VCO. In operation, the DC voltage forces the VCO to run at exactly the same frequency as the crystal-controlled reference oscillator. Should the VCO drift or change frequency the deviation would be detected by the frequency comparator and its DC voltage would either increase or decrease, changing the frequency of the VCO back to the exact frequency of the crystal-controlled oscillator. Thus, the basic phase-locked loop demonstrates that a voltage-controlled oscillator can be made to run at an extremely stable, reference-determined frequency.

To see how the phase-locked loop system works in TV tuning systems, we must modify the basic circuit, as shown in Fig. 7-17. Now, a frequency divider stage has been added to the loop between the voltage-controlled oscillator and frequency comparator. In Fig. 7-17, the frequency divider shown is a divide-by-two circuit. This means that the frequency sample reaching the frequency comparator is now only one-half the frequency of the crystal-controlled reference. Thus, the DC voltage from the frequency comparator will increase or decrease until the voltage-controlled oscillator runs at twice the reference oscillator frequency. When the voltage-controlled oscillator frequency sample reaches the frequency comparator, it again matches the crystal-controlled oscillator reference frequency and the loop is stabilized. Thus, the VCO is now operating at twice the frequency of the crystal-controlled oscillator.

Let's now study Fig. 7-18 as we dig into these tuning systems a little deeper. In Fig. 7-17, the divide-by-two stage has been replaced with a divide-by-N stage. The frequency divider in Fig. 7-18 is therefore capable of dividing the VCO frequency sample by multiple numbers of division. With the reference frequency known, the divide-by-N stage can be programmed by logic circuitry to divide by the number of divisions that correspond to specific VCO frequencies. The circuit now becomes a frequency synthesizer, capable of producing a wide spectrum of VCO frequencies, all referenced to one crystal-controlled oscillator and, thus, extremely stable. For example, if the reference oscillator frequency were 1 MHz and we wanted the VCO to run at the correct local oscillator frequency for channel 2 (101 MHz), the logic circuitry would prog-

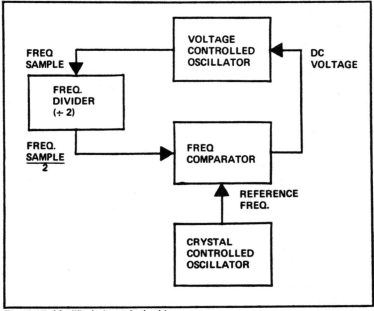

Fig. 7-17. Modified phase-locked loop.

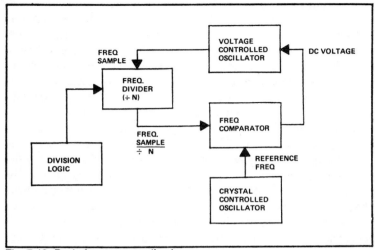

Fig. 7-18. Basic frequency synthesizer.

ram the divider circuitry to divide the frequency sample by a factor of 101 times.

In the actual circuitry of the tuner control module, the reference oscillator consists of discrete, crystal-controlled components. The programmable divider is a high-speed IC that has the division logic and frequency comparator contained in the NC6410 chip. The VCO, of course, corresponds to the local oscillators in the VHF and UHF tuners.

The tuner control module block diagram is shown in Fig. 7-19. The frequency synthesizer, EIC20, accepts three types of inputs. One is a 4-MHz reference frequency from the reference oscillator stage composed of EIC50 and EX50. Another frequency sample is received from the local oscillators in the VHF and UHF tuners. It also receives channel selection logic from the remote decoder module and front panel keyboard.

The frequency sample from the tuners is first amplified by three transistor stages—EQ1, 2 and 3. It is then divided by a factor of 64 by EIC1. Finally, the frequency sample is divided again by a programmable divider stage—EIC5, 10 and then by 15.

The number of divisions performed by the programmable divider is determined by commands from EIC20. The division commands, in turn, are developed in EIC20 from the channel selection logic it receives.

The channel selection logic entering the tuner control module is first processed before entering EIC20. The logic interface cir-

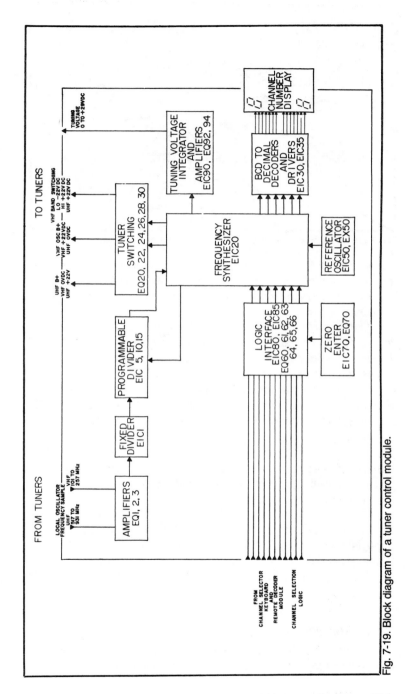

Fig. 7-19. Block diagram of a tuner control module.

211

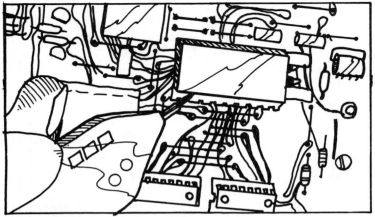

Fig. 7-20. Logic probe check on a microprocessor chip.

cuitry, EIC80, 85 and EQ60 through 66, convert the decimal logic into a seven-line code, acceptable to EIC20. In addition, the logic interface circuitry provides impedance matching to the inputs of the frequency synthesizer.

Outputs from the frequency synthesizer are DC voltages that control the tuners and binary-coded decimal logic that is used to develop channel number indication. The tuner switching stage receives commands from the EIC20 as a result of the channel selection logic fed into the chip. Switching voltages are produced which activate either the UHF or VHF tuner with B+ voltage. A VHF high/low bandswitching voltage is also generated in the tuner switching stage.

The DC tuning voltage, fed to the local oscillators and other tuned circuits in the tuners, is developed in the circuitry composed of EIC90, EQ92, and EQ94. This voltage is dependent on the frequency synthesis process.

The final output from the EIC20 chip is binary-coded decimal information that corresponds to the channel number selected. The hobbyist shown in Fig. 7-20 is checking these binary bits with a logic probe. This data is converted first to decimal and then to seven-segment logic by EIC30 and EIC35. These outputs drive the LED channel numbers.

System Troubleshooting

Some of the MOS digital devices used in this remote system can be damaged by static charges, so when troubleshooting these

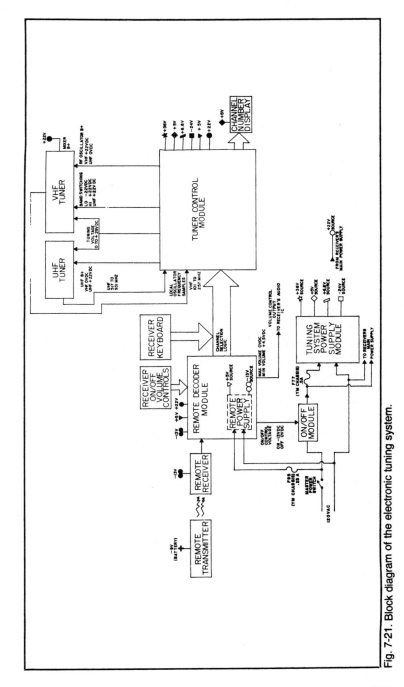

Fig. 7-21. Block diagram of the electronic tuning system.

MOS circuits, special precautions must be taken. Because MOS devices will not leak off static charges, their handling is much more critical than other ICs. MOS devices are usually packaged in conductive foam material. When handling an MOS device, you should touch a grounded object to discharge body capacitance before touching a MOS component. When soldering around a MOS device, the tip of the iron should be grounded. Of course, a static-sensitive component should not be inserted or removed from the circuit with the power on. With electronic tuning systems, this means that the power cord should be unplugged before any modules are replaced. Remember that most of the power sources of the tuning systems still operate, but the set is only turned off.

Locating defective modules in the tuning system is usually quite easy, because of the nature of digital circuitry. Digital logic circuitry lends itself to analytical analysis far more readily than most analog circuitry. Faults usually give positive indications. A circuit either works right or it will not operate at all. The marginal failure condition, so many times encountered in analog TV sets, is a rare bird in digital logic systems.

The technique becomes apparent when we put this into actual practice. Note the block diagram shown in Fig. 7-21. In one example, the TV set has no volume control with its manual controls, but volume control was normal when the remote control was used. If all other remote functions perform normally, then two areas should be checked out: Either the remote decoder module is defective or the ON/OFF VOLUME control unit and plug connections of the set are faulty. Use an ohmmeter to check controls.

For another example, stations cannot be selected with the remote transmitter and all other controls are operating correctly. A block diagram analysis reveals that the remote decoder module would be the suspected area.

Naturally, some failure modes do not lend themselves to this type of troubleshooting logic. For instance, the receiver may have a no raster and loss of sound symptom. This condition requires choosing between the remote decoder module, on/off module, TV chassis fault and power supply troubles in the main TV chassis. A combination of observations and DC voltage checks is necessary to correctly diagnose the defective module for this type of malfunction.

Chapter 8
Video Cassette Recorder
and Videodisc Player Servicing

In this chapter we will touch on a few selected digital/logic and PLL circuits found in video play/record machines. We will also be looking at servo controls and tracking systems.

SONY VCR SYSTEM

This section will cover the SONY VCR Betamax format and helical scan system. Information on the chroma signal processor and modulator section will be dealt with. Then we will look at record/play head timing pulses, servo controls and tracking systems.

Chroma Signal Processing

The chroma record signal is processed with IC2 (CX-133A) which is located on the YC-L board tha is located on the bottom of the machine. The chroma record system operates as a record acc (automatic chroma level control), as a color killer and performs the frequency down conversion to 688 Hz. Referring to the block diagram in Fig. 8-1, you will see that the video signal is fed to a 3.58-MHz bandpass filter at the same point where the chroma signal is separated.

The filter output is then fed to the acc gain-controlled amplifier. This circuit is similar to the acc control range in some TV chassis. This amplifier controls the gain to keep the burst signal at a constant level.

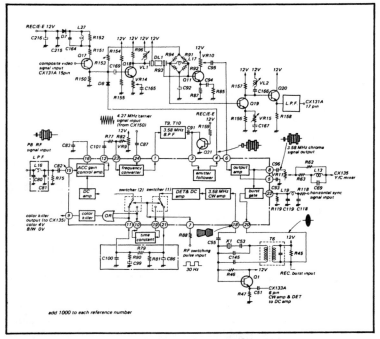

Fig. 8-1. Playback chroma signal process circuit CX-136A.

The acc output goes to a frequency converter and burst gate circuit. Also going to this circuit is a delayed horizontal sync input pulse. This opens the burst gate at the proper time to allow only the burst through. This burst signal is then coupled to the burst transformer and then to a crystal ringing filter circuit which converts the burst signal to a CW signal. The amplitude of this CW signal is proportional to the amplitude of the burst signal and is fed into pin 6 of IC 2. The normal 3.58-MHz CW signal is shown in Fig. 802. The filtered CW signal is then amplified to a level high enough to drive the acc detector circuit. The acc peak detector detects the CW signal and compares it with the reference voltage to obtain an error voltage. The acc output level is adjusted by changing the reference voltage. In essence, the converted chroma signal recorded on the tape retains the same level relationship as did the original chroma signal. If the recorded video tape chroma level is different from the original TV program (color too strong or too weak), this circuit may be defective.

The scope can be used to check for waveforms shown on the block diagram in Fig. 8-1. A video signal should be found at pin 13 of

IC2. A delayed horizontal sync pulse is at pin 10. The 3.58-MHz CW signal is at pin 6. And a 4.27-MHz input signal is at pin 16. There should also be a 3.58-MHz chroma ouput at pin 18 and a 688-kHz chroma output at pin 15 of IC 2. If all input signals check correctly on the scope, then IC 2 could be defective. Of course, make sure that all DC power-supply voltages are correct.

Chroma Playback

In playback mode, the rf signal is received from the rf playback amplifier. This signal contains both the chroma and Y-FM signal. This signal is routed through a low-pass filter, which rejects the Y-FM signal, extracting only the 688-kHz chroma signal.

The 688-kHz signal is fed to an acc gain-controlled amplifier. The DC voltage, obtained by detecting the playback burst signal, is fed to the gain-controlled amplifier. A feedback loop thus formed adjusts the gain of the acc amplifier so that the burst signal level remains constant. Because separate capacity stage circuits for the acc detection output are provided for each channel, the acc loops are independent for each of the two heads, so no chroma output level is noted, even if a large level difference exists between the two head outputs.

The signal now passes through the 3.58-mHz filter and then to an emitter-follower circuit—pin 4 of IC 4—and is coupled to the

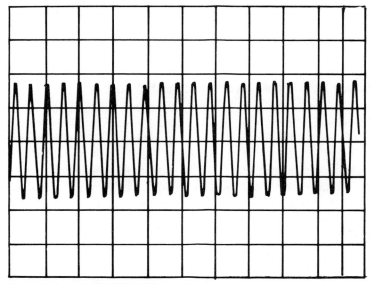

Fig. 8-2. Normal 3.58-MHz CW signal.

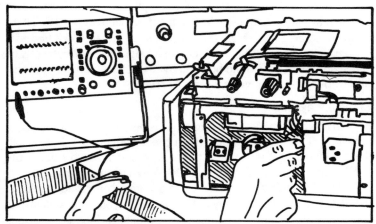

Fig. 8-3. Oscilloscope being used to check out the VCR.

comb filter, where the cross-talk component is removed. The comb filter output is fed to an output amplifier. From the amplifier, the signal is passed on to the Y/C mixer. The hobbyist in Fig. 8-3 is using the scope to check waveforms on the RS-L board.

Countdown Circuits

The sync separator, horizontal pulse generator and divide-by-44 countdown circuit form a part of the afc loop. This circuit, shown in Fig. 8-4, is located on the YC-L board. The scope is used to check on operation of the multivibrator and the divide-by-44 countdown circuit.

Carrier Signal Phase Inverter and Burst ID Circuits

IC 1007, shown in Fig. 8-5, contains a carrier signal phase inverter circuit and a burst ID circuit. The carrier phase inverter consists of a flip-flop and switching circuit. A 4.27-MHz carrier signal is phase-split by the phase splitter transformer T15. The output from the secondary of T15 is fed to the switching circuit via pins 8 and 9. The normal phase 4.27-MHz carrier is fed to pin 8 and the out-of-phase carrier to pin 9. The dual-trace scope probes can be connected to pin 9 and 8 of IC 1007 to check on the 4.27-MHz signal and for a phase-shift from T15. The switching circuit is driven by the flip-flop output and the rf switching pulse, both of which are fed to the switcher through an OR gate. As shown in Fig. 8-5, the flip-flop is triggered by a horizontal pulse and toggles at a 1 horizontal rate. The output of this flip-flop and the 30-MHz rf switching

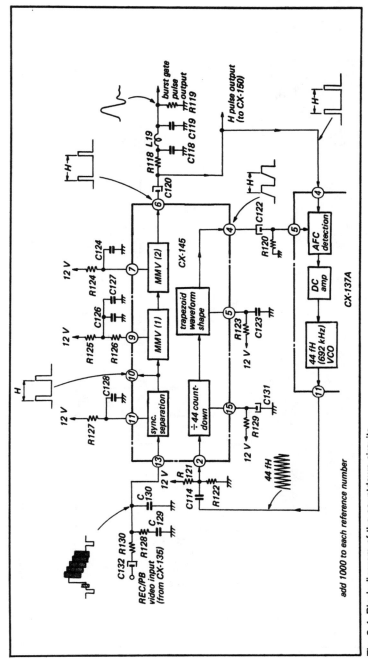

Fig. 8-4. Block diagram of the countdown circuits.

219

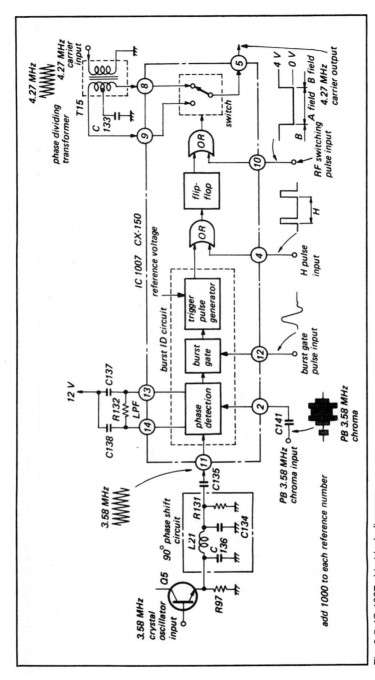

Fig. 8-5. IC 1007 chip block diagram.

pulse are applied to the OR gate. The output of the gate is waveform 7 in Fig. 8-6. The 4.27-MHz carrier output from pin 5 is fed to the chroma frequency converter circuits of the record and playback systems. Check with the scope at pin 5 for the 4.27-MHz signal to see if the IC switch is working properly.

The 688-MHz recorded chroma signal is phase-inverted line-by-line on every track recorded by the A head. When this signal is recovered, it is necessary that the switching phase of the 4.27-MHz carrier is phase inverted line-by-line is the same as used in recording. Because the switching is done by a flip-flop toggled by a horizontal sync pulse, a signal loss caused by dropout would mean there is a good probability that the flip-flop would be in the wrong state at any given line of playback. To prevent this, a circuit is provided which determines the state of the flip-flop relative to the playback signal on a line-by-line basis and resets it if required. The circuit is a *burst phase ID circuit* that compares the phase of the playback burst signal against the 3.58-MHz stable crystal reference oscillator. Another scope check point would then be pin 11 of IC 1007 for the 3.58-MHz oscillator signal. This 3.58-MHz signal is a burst phase reference in the playback mode. When the apc loop is locked, there is a 90-degree phase difference between the playback burst signal from the reference oscillator. The output signal from the reference oscillator is fed through a 90-degree phase-shift network before it goes to the phase comparator. This places both the oscillator signal and the playback burst signal at the same phase.

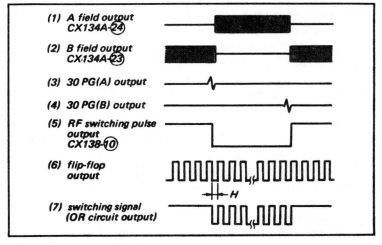

Fig. 8-6. OR gate waveforms.

Whenever a phase inversion occurs between the two signals, because of misorientation of the flip-flop, a large output error signal is produced at the phase detector. This error signal pulse is fed to the flip-flop through the other input of the OR gate than that through which the flip-flop is normally toggled by the horizontal sync pulse. It forces the flip-flop into the correct initial state.

Servo and Pulse Systems

The head servo system is operating while all of the video signal processing is taking place. Refer to Fig. 8-7 for a block diagram of servo circuits. The composite video input signal is fed to a sync separator which has the vertical sync pulses at its output. A second signal is fed to the servo circuits from the spinning disc of the video heads. This signal (called the PG or pulse generator pulse) is generated by a permanent magnet located on the video disc assembly which passes over a pickup coil as the heads rotate. The phase between the PG pulse and the vertical sync pulse is compared, and the speed of the head disc is varied until the two signals are in phase with each other.

The vertical signal is also fed to a stage that divides the frequency in half. This 30-Hz signal is fed to a recording head along the tape travel path. This head records the 30-Hz control track that will be used as a reference to control the servo circuits during playback.

The head drum is belt driven by an AC synchronous motor. The drums free-running speed is set slightly higher than desired, and speed regulation is achieved by applying braking action. This brake is controlled by the servo system. The servo system controls the speed of the head drum only. The pulse system produces switching signals used in switching between the two heads and in switching the 4.27-MHz carrier. The position relationship of the video heads and the pulse generator coils (30 PG coils) is shown in Fig. 8-8.

The two video heads are mounted 180 degrees apart on the periphery of the head disc. The magnetic pole pieces and PG coils are also mounted on the disc. The 30 PG (A) signal is used in the drum servo system, while the 30 PG (A and B) signals are used to produce the rf switching pulse. Use an oscilloscope to check for proper pulses from the PG coils.

The pulse generated by the 30 PG (A) coil is amplified by the 30 PG (A) amplifier and from there to both the lock PG delay multivibrator and delay MMV2. Both delay multivibrators are one-shot,

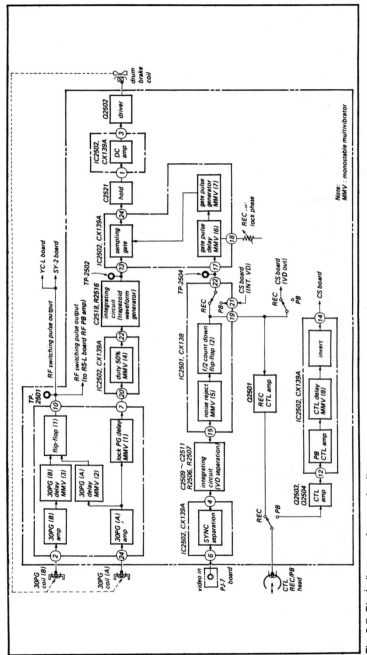

Fig. 8-7. Block diagram of servo circuits.

toggled by the 30 PG (A) pulse, and both produce rectangular-shaped output pulses. The output from MMV1 toggles a second one-shot, MMV4, which squares the signal into a 50-percent duty cycle waveform. The output from MMV4 is passed through an integrator network which converts the square-wave into a trapezoidal waveform. Use the scope to see if the pulses are being processed properly in the flip-flops and countdown chips found in the servo system.

The composite video is fed to the sync separator and then passed through an integrator network that removes only the vertical sync pulses. This is fed to a one-shot in the MMV5 which eliminates noise. The output from MMV5 toggles a flip-flop that divides and shapes the signal into a 30-MHz square wave. This signal is used in the record mode as the control (CTL) signal. It is also applied to a gate pulse to delay the one-shot MMV6, which in turn toggles MMV7, the *gate pulse generator*. The gate pulse is fed to the sample gate along with the trapezoidal 30 PG (A) signal. In the sample gate, the two signals are phase-compared, and the sample voltage is stored in a hold circuit. This stored voltage is amplified by DC amplifiers and controls the drum brake coil driver transistor. To lock up the servo on playback, a 300-Hz oscillator is phase-locked to the line frequency and counted down by a one-tenth countdown circuit which will form a 30-Hz square wave at test point 4604. This is a good scope test point to go to if you encounter servo problems. This pulse is transferred to the tracking control circuit where it becomes the servo reference voltage during playback.

The servo control circuits of a video recorder simply compare two signals to indicate that the video heads are in the correct position during both recording and playback. During recording, the two signals are the vertical sync pulses and the head position signal (PG pulses). The two signals should arrive at the servo comparison circuits at the same time. A dual-trace scope is a must for evaluating this action. If they are not properly timed, the servo circuits will adjust the rotational speed of the video heads until the two signals correspond.

During playback, the same head reference pulse (PG pulse) is compared with the output of the control track head. Again, the two signals are compared and the speed of the rotating head disc is adjusted until the two pulses are properly timed. Signal pulse injection may also be used to analyze some sections of the servo circuits that are difficult to analyze using the scope or other troubleshooting techniques.

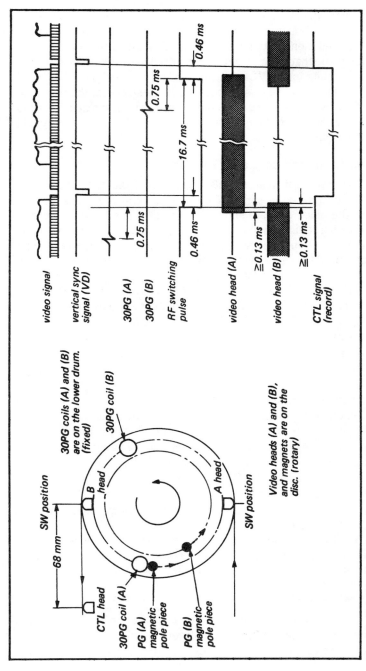

Fig. 8-8. Relationship between heads and PG coils.

225

Signal injection works very well when combined with an oscilloscope for signal tracing. Just inject the subber signal at the input to a stage and monitor the resulting signal at the output of the same stage or one that is supposed to be controlled by the injected signal. Many circuits in the VCR require that both the amplitude and the waveshape of the signals be correct. In these cases, the use of an oscilloscope is essential. The combination of both signal tracing and signal injection in many cases provides the best analyzing techniques.

Servo Timing and Generating Circuits

The vertical sync signals, separated from the video input signal, becomes the servo reference signal in the record mode. Note the block diagram shown in Fig. 8-9. The filter rejects the chroma burst signal and high frequency noise. The video output is connected as an input to the RS-L board. If you have servo and timing trouble, check with a scope and see if you are getting the proper video signal input at this point.

The video signal is sync-separated in the circuit between pins 6 and 4 of IC 502. The sync separation circuit consists of a feedback clamp circuit for sag correction and a switching amplifier. An RC integrator circuit separates the vertical sync from the sync separator output and triggers the noise elimination one-shot, MMV 5, via SW (1) of IC 501. SW (1) switches to the pin 15 side for a zero-volt input at pin 16 and to the pin 14 side for 12 volts. The noise elimination one-shot, MMV(5), eliminates noise by the fact that a one-shot, once toggled, cannot be toggled again until after it has reset itself. The external circuit at pin 17 is the time constant network for MMV 5. The 60-Hz vertical signal is divided into a 30-Hz square wave in the divide-by-two flip-flop. The 30-Hz square wave passes through SW (3) and appears as the gate signal output at pin 22.

The negative-going transition of the flip-flop output becomes the servo reference phase that is used on the video tape control track. The proper phasing of the integrated pulse will appear at pin 9 of IC 502. Thus, the internal vertical reference signal becomes the gate signal for control of the drum servo.

THE MAGNAVOX MODEL VH 8000 VIDEO PLAYER

In this section we will look at some of the many new circuits found in the Magnavox Videodisc player. This unit uses a laser beam to recover video and audio information from a disc to produce high

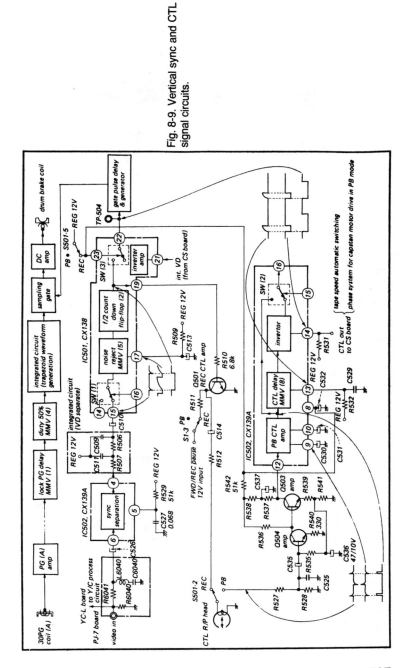

Fig. 8-9. Vertical sync and CTL signal circuits.

227

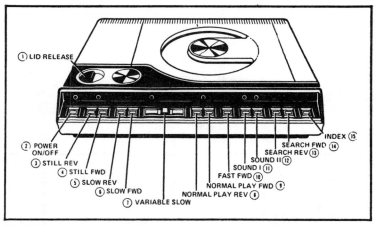

Fig. 8-10. Front panel view of the Magnavox Videodisc player.

quality pictures and sound on any color TV receiver. The front panel view of the VH 8000 is shown in Fig. 8-10.

Servo Controls

The servo control circuitry performs the following functions in the videodisc machine.

■ Turntable motor control.
■ Tangential tracking mirror control.
■ Radial tracking mirror control.
■ Slide drive control.
■ Objective lens control (focus).
■ Turn-on sequence logic.

The turntable motor control and the tangential mirror control operate together. Their purpose is to keep the track movement over the light beam at a constant velocity. Refer to Fig. 8-11 for the complete laser optical path. Errors in the velocity of the track over the beam become timing errors in the video signal. Speed errors can be caused by an unstable turntable motor speed or eccentric rotation caused by an off-centered hole. An inherent 30-Hz error exists due to the eccentricity of the tracks. They are actually a spiral instead of perfect circles.

Correct motor speed is maintained by comparing the horizontal video sync pulses with a locally generated crystal-controlled oscillator. However, even with correct motor speed, instantaneous speed errors occur as the track travels an eccentric path. These speed errors occur at a 30-Hz rate (the speed of a standard play disc). The 30-Hz eccentricity errors and other momentary speed variations are corrected by controlling the moveable tangential mirror.

The block diagram in Fig. 8-12 shows the arrangement used to compensate for time errors. A locally generated 15,734-Hz oscillator is used as a master reference. The composite video signal serves as an indicator of the disc speed. If the disc is too fast, the sync pulses will be too close together. Slower than normal speed causes the sync pulses to be farther apart.

The turntable motor cannot change speed instantaneously, so it responds only to gradual speed errors. The tangential mirror, however, can move very quickly. It responds to the higher frequency errors, such as the 30-Hz speed changes. An electronic tangential loopswitch is used to take the tangential mirror out of the circuit whenever the turntable motor is not at the correct speed.

A sync separator strips the sync from the composite video signal and feeds negative-going composite sync to the filtered sync generator. This generator simply generates a new sync pulse with the same frequency as the original, but with filtering added during the time between sync pulses. In this manner, no unwanted spikes between sync pulses can upset circuit operation.

The filtered sync is fed to the motor phase detector along with a pulse from the reference oscillator. The output of the motor phase

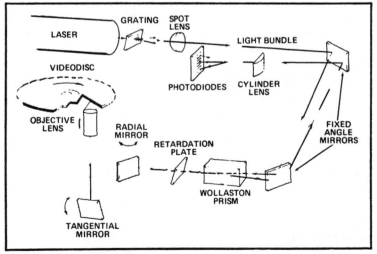

Fig. 8-11. Optical path drawing.

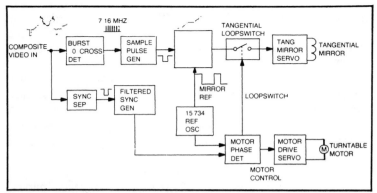

Fig. 8-12. Block diagram of tangential and motor drive.

detector is fed to the motor drive servo that spins the turntable motor. If the phase of the filtered sync should ever drift with respect to the reference pulse, the motor phase detector will cause the motor drive servo to correct the motor speed.

Another output from the motor phase detector is used to control the electronic tangential loopswitch. If the sync frequency is not equal to the reference frequency, the tangential loopswitch is opened, taking the tangential mirror out of the circuit. The mirror will remain inactive until such time as the motor resumes its correct speed.

The composite video signal is also used to create a reference for the tangential mirror control. However, the sync pulse cannot be used because its leading edge is not precise enough. Therefore, a sample pulse is generated, using the burst as a precise reference.

The composite signal is applied to the burst 0 cross detector. This detector creates a pulse each time the sinusoidal burst signal passes through zero. The result is a 7.16-MHz chain of very accurate timing pulses during the burst time. These are applied to the sample pulse generator. The generator creates the sample pulse which begins at the same time as one of the zero cross burst pulses. The same zero cross pulse always triggers the sample pulse on each horizontal line. The sample pulse thus becomes a very precise reference for the horizontal frequency of the composite video signal.

The sample pulse and the mirror reference pulse from the reference oscillator are both fed to the sample and hold tangential phase detector. The mirror reference pulse starts a ramp voltage during every horizontal line. When the sample pulse is present, the ramp is stopped and a sample is taken off the ramp voltage at that point. Any phase shift in the sample pulse (indicating a speed change) will cause the sample to be taken at a higher or lower point on the ramp. The sample voltage is stored and becomes the correction voltage applied to the tangential mirror servo through the closed loopswitch. Because the sample pulse and ramp occur at the horizontal rate, the correction voltage is updated 15,734 times per second. The largest component of correction occurs at a 30-Hz rate because of the elliptical tracks and the 30-Hz speed of the videodisc. The timing waveforms and their relationship to each other are shown in Fig. 8-13.

Reference Control Module Circuit

The block diagram shown in Fig. 8-14 is of the reference control module. The composite video signal input at pin 17 is fed to the composite sync and video clipper. This circuit clips the video

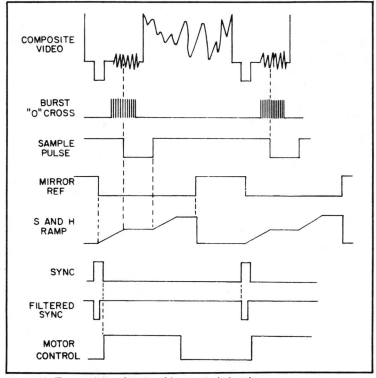

Fig. 8-13. Tangential and motor drive control signals.

signal at two different levels. One clipper creates the clipped video signal, which is sent out pin 2 to the mode control module. The mode control module samples this output only at the proper times to retrieve the digital code information for the picture number. Another clipper removes the composite sync and feeds it to the mode control module at pin 3 and to a filtered sync generator. The mode control module uses the composite sync signal to generate timing pulses to place the picture number in the upper left-hand corner of the screen. The filtered sync generator merely regenerates a new sync signal with the same frequency as the original but with filtering added during the time between pulses. In case of faulty sync from a dropout, a dropout protector will reinsert a new sync signal to replace the missing one. The filtered sync exits the module at pin 10 and is also applied simultaneously to the clamp gate and burst gate pulse generator and to one input of the motor phase detector. The clamp gate pulse is used to clamp the video to the correct DC level on the video processor module. It also gates the burst out of the video on the color separator module.

The other input to the motor phase detector is the 15,734-Hz reference signal. This signal is derived from a 4.53-MHz reference oscillator that is divided down to obtain the 15,734-Hz reference frequency. These two inputs are compared in the motor phase detector and develop the motor control signal at pin 11 and the tangential loop switch voltage at pin 15. The 15,734-Hz reference signal at pin 1 is also used as the mirror phase detector module.

Drive and Track Control Logic Circuits

The block diagram in Fig. 8-15 shows the radial drive and track jump logic circuits. During normal play, the high-frequency com-

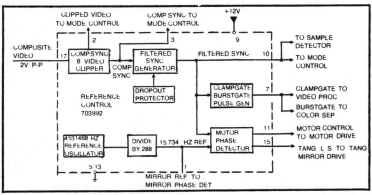

Fig. 8-14. Reference control module circuit.

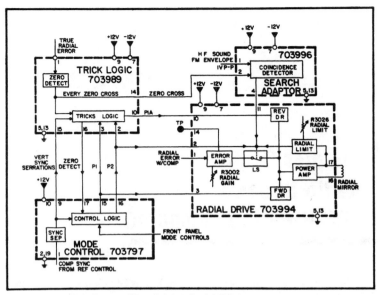

Fig. 8-15. Radial drive and track jump logic circuits.

pensated radial error signal from the preamp module is fed to an error amp on the radial drive module. This stage is gain-controlled by R3002. The error signal is coupled through the closed radial loop switch to a complementary type power amp which drives the radial mirror. The radial drive module also has the radial limit circuit. This circuit sets the maximum allowable tilt of the radial mirror and is adjustable by R3026. Should this limit be reached, the radial limit circuit will open the loop switch and allow the mirror to fall back to its center position.

The trick logic, search adaptor and mode control modules are only used during special modes of operation. An input from the front panel buttons is sent to the mode control module. Immediately after vertical sync, the track jump logic generates P2 simultaneously with P1 or P1A. The sequence at which P1 and P1A are generated depends on the particular mode of operation.

The true radial error signal from the preamp is sent to a zero cross detector on the track logic module. This detector creates an output each time the radial signal passes through zero. The zero cross signal is compared with the vertical sync serrations in the zero cross logic to develop a zero detect signal. This signal is used by the track jump logic on the mode control module to switch from P1 to P1A, or vice versa.

Chapter 9
Radio Shack's
TRS-80 Microcomputer

In this chapter we will take a look at Radio Shack's very popular TRS-80 microcomputer system. Some brief system operation information will be given to familarize you with this system. Troubleshooting information and tips will be given for the RAM, ROM, CPU, video divider chain, system clock, power supply, address lines, keyboard and video processing systems. Also included in this chapter are the complete schematic diagrams for the TRS-80 and some section isolation troubleshooting flow charts.

In this first section we will take a brief look at the basic operation of the Radio Shack model TRS-80 microcomputer. Some basic theory of operation along with block diagrams will be covered. Some troubleshooting tips and system flowcharts will also be given. Also, unit disassembly and power supply checks will be discussed. The Radio Shack TRS-80 microcomputer system is shown in Fig. 9-1.

TRS-80 SYSTEM BLOCK DIAGRAM

You will find the integrated circuits contained in the TRS-80 can be broken down into 10 major sections. The system block diagram in Fig. 9-2 shows these units as they are related to other sections. The heart of the system is the CPU (central processing unit). Most of the leads on the CPU are data lines and address lines. The CPU tells the address bus where the data it wants is located, and the data bus is a good place for the information to come back to

Fig. 9-1. The Radio Shack TRS-80 microcomputer.

the CPU. The address lines are outputs from the CPU. They never receive data or addresses from other sections. The data lines, on the other hand, can give or receive data.

ROM Operation

If the CPU has to be the heart of the system, the ROM (read-only memory) could very well be considered the brain. The ROM tells the CPU what to do, how to do it and where to put the data after each operation. Without the ROM, the CPU would just function or run as a pulse generator. When power is first applied to

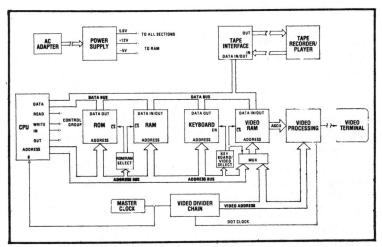

Fig. 9-2. Block diagram of the TRS-80 microcomputer.

235

the system, the CPU outputs an address to the ROM that locates the first instruction of the CPU. The ROM fires back the first instruction and then the two start communicating. In less than a second, the CPU, under ROM control, performs all the housekeeping required to start up the system. It then flashes a READY on the screen.

If the CPU misses that first piece of ROM data, it may become unglued. It may tell the ROM that it is ready to load a tape so the ROM tells it how to do that. The tape recorder turns on. But since the CPU is now playing games in the video memory, the tape is not needed. Because the CPU operates at about 2 MHz, these digital foulups seem instantaneous.

You can just think of the CPU as the work horse and the ROM as the boss. The ROM tells the CPU how to do it, when to do it and where it was placed.

RAM Operation

The next major section in Fig. 9-3 is the RAM (Random Access Memory). This memory is where the CPU can file data it may not need until later. The RAM is also the place where the programs are kept. If you tell the computer to count to 7500, the CPU stores your instructions in the RAM.

The CPU tells the ROM someone wants in. The ROM tells the CPU to go to the keyboard and find out who. The CPU finds out, tells the ROM it's the number one chief. The ROM tells the CPU to find out what the chief wants. The CPU tells the ROM that the chief wants us to RUN. The ROM tells the CPU to go to RAM and find out what the chief wants done. The CPU says the chief wants to count to 7500. The ROM tells the CPU how to do it. After it's done, the ROM tells the CPU to find out what to do with it. The CPU informs the ROM that the 7500 count must go on the video display and be saved. The ROM tells the CPU how to put it on the display and then tells it to store the 7500 somewhere in RAM and then remember where it is. The CPU tells the ROM that the job is completed. The ROM tells the CPU to monitor the keyboard in case the chief wants a program run.

The CPU looks to the ROM for instructions. The CPU then follows the instructions from ROM and looks to the keyboard, then the RAM. In all cases, the CPU applies address locations to the ROM, RAM and keyboard. The data lines are then checked for input data that correspond to these address locations. In case of an output from the CPU to RAM, the CPU selects the address, puts data on the data lines and then instructs the RAM to store the data that is on the data lines.

Make a note that the CPU only communicates with all other sections of the computer. If it is told by ROM to store an item from ROM into RAM, the CPU can't make the RAM receive ROM data directly. Instead, the CPU takes the data from ROM and then sends it to RAM. The CPU must act as an intermediary. The reason for this is that the CPU is the only section that can address locations and pass data to all other sections.

Keyboard and Video Processing

The keyboard section is not necessary as far as the CPU is concerned, but it is very necessary for data to be fed in by the operator. The keyboard is used for making known your instructions to the CPU. The opposite is true for the video RAM. In this case, the CPU wants to tell us it needs data or it may want to show us the result of a complex calculation. So the request for more information or the result is stuffed into the video RAM. Anything in video RAM is automatically displayed on the terminal. The video processing section handles this. Data in the video RAM is in ASCII. Converting ASCII into the alphanumeric symbols we recognize is the job of the video processor. A ROM contains all of the dot patterns. The ASCII locates the character pattern, and the video processor sends it out to the terminal.

Video Divider Chain

Composite video going on to a video terminal is extremely complex. Aside from the video signal, there is the horizontal and vertical sync. These signals must be very stable and be outputted in the correct sequence. The CPU is very busy, so the video divider chain handles the TV signal to the monitor. It generates the sync signals and addresses the video RAM in a logical order so that the video processor can handle video data efficiently.

Note the block under the video RAM labeled MUX. This is short for multiplexer. It acts somewhat like a multipole, multiposition switch. When the video divider chain is in control, the MUX is switched so that only addresses from the divider chain are directed to the video RAM. The CPU may need to read or write data into the video RAM. If so, the MUX is switched so that the CPU has control over the address of the video RAM. After the CPU is finished, the addressing task is reassigned to the divider chain.

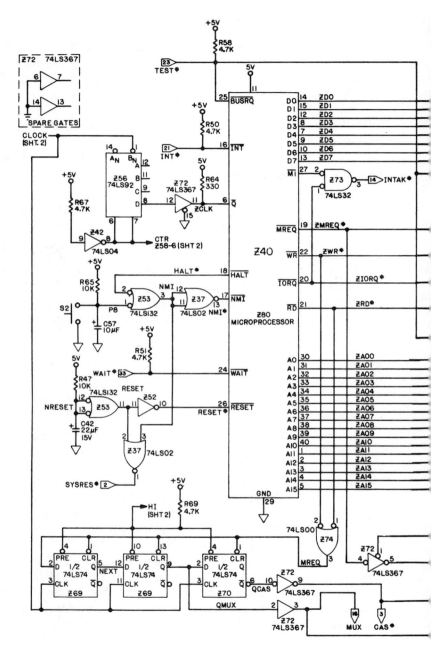

Fig. 9-3. TRS-80 schematic (first part).

NOTE:
1. Z13 THRU Z20 ARE RANDOM ACCESS MEMORIES
(4K, 8K OR 16K RAM'S)

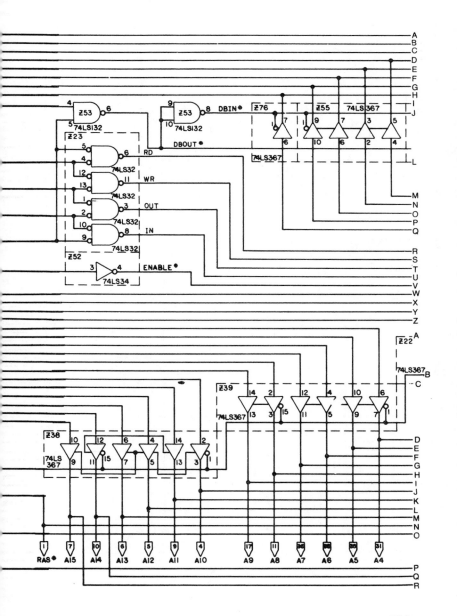

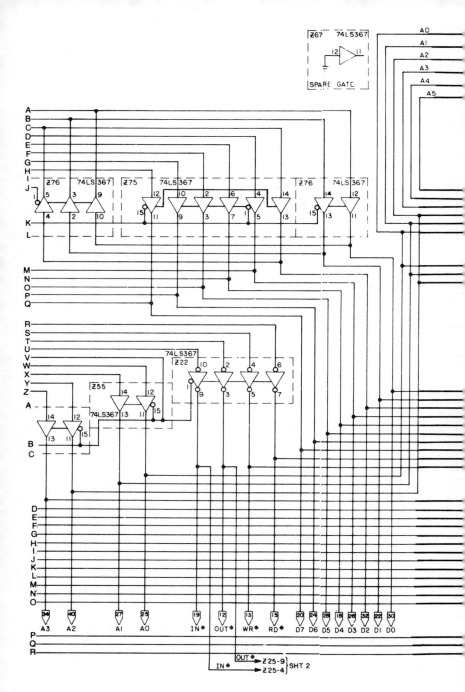

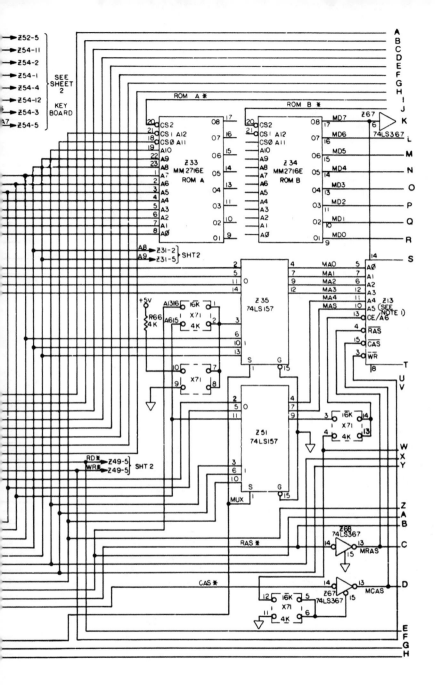

241

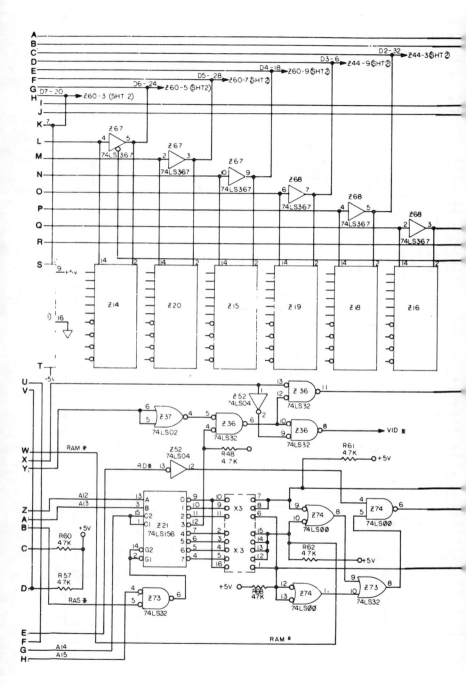

242

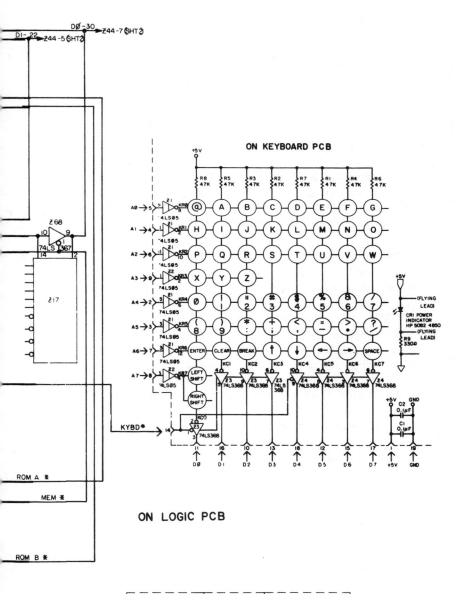

ON KEYBOARD PCB

ON LOGIC PCB

243

System Clock

The system clock circuit is shown in Fig. 9-4. Y1 is a fundamental-cut 10.6445-MHz crystal. It is a series resonant circuit consisiting of two inverters. Z42, pins 1 and 2, and 3 and 4, form two inverting amplifiers. Feedback between the inverters is supplied by C43, a 47-pF capacitor. R46 and R52 force the inverters used in the oscillator to operate in their linear region.

The waveform at pin 5 of Z42 will resemble a sine wave at 10.6445 MHz. The oscillator should not be measured at this point, however, because of the loading effects that test equipment would have at this node. Z42, pin 6, is the output of the oscillator buffer. Clock measurements may be made at this point. The output of the buffer is applied to three main sections: the CPU timing circuit, the video chain and the video processing circuit.

Power Supply System

The TRS-80 requires three voltage-supply levels: A +12 volts at 350 milliamps, +5 volts at about 1.2 amps and a −5 volts at 1 milliamp.

The +12 and −5 volts are needed by the RAM. All other devices require +5 volts. The +12 and +5 volt supplies are regulated and currect-protected against shorts. The −5 volts supply is not as critical as the other two supplies, and it uses a single zener diode for regulation. The stepped-down AC voltage is supplied by an AC adaptor. The adaptor has a transformer with one primary and two secondary windings.

The secondary windings are both center-tapped. One is rated at 14 volts AC at 1 amp. This winding is used for the +5 and −5 volt supplies. The other winding has diodes connected, and it outputs 19.8 VDC at about 350 milliamps. This circuit is used for the 12-volt supply. All voltage outputs and center taps are brought into the power input jack.

The +12 Volt Power Supply. Unregulated DV voltage for the +12 volt supply is inputted at pin 2 of the power jack. When the POWER switch is closed, the output voltage is about 20 volts because of action of the filter capacitor. This voltage is then fed to a transistor and regulator Z2. Figure 9-5 shows a simplified diagram of the internal circuitry for the 723 regulator chip.

Power Supply Checks for the TRS-80. Most problems that result in loss of power-supply voltage will be associated with solder shorts, component shorts or defective power supply adaptors. Usually, the power supply will not be damaged by a short

244

because the regulators use current-limiting with foldback. A solder short or shorted component does not have to be in the power section to cause a supply problem. The short can be anywhere.

Should you be missing +12 volts and +5 volts, measure the voltage across R18. This resistor monitors the current flow from the +12 volt supply. If the voltage reads about 0.6 volts, the +12 volt bus is in foldback and has shut itself off. Since the +12 volt bus is shutoff, you will not have +5 volts because the +5 volt regulator is referenced to the +12 volt output. You must now locate and remove the short on the +12 volt bus before anything will work.

If the −5 volt supply is not present, first confirm that there is ample negative voltage on the adaptor side of R19. See if R19 is dropping all of the voltage. If so, you have a −5 volt bus short.

The +12 volt and the −5 volt supplies are used by the system RAM. If you have problems with either of these two, suspect a RAM short. See if you can find a RAM that generates more heat than the others. Use a temperature probe for this check.

Pull all RAMS and retest. If all of the power supplies are now good, turn off the power and re-install one RAM. Turn on the power and retest. Install each RAM until you find one that loads down the power supply. Remove the faulty RAM and continue to check out the other ICs. There may be more than one shorted device.

A short on the +5 volt bus can be a really tough one to find. Unless you can see the short, you will have to cut PC runs to isolate a section. Once a section is isolated, you will probably have to make other cuts to find the short. And remember to repair the cuts. These runs carry considerable current, so use solid 22 guage wire to repair the cuts. If you find a dead +12 volt bus, check the heat sink of transistor Q1. The hardware holding the heat sink may become loose and shorted the leads of Q1.

Table 9-1 lists the voltages found around Z1 and Z2 for a normal operating unit. These measurements were taken when the +12 volt supply was adjusted for 12 volts and the −5 volt supply was adjusted to 5 volts.

ISOLATION OF A DEFECTIVE COMPUTER SECTION

One of the toughest problems to section-isolate is a screen full of junk at power on. This is a display with all character positions filled with either alphanumerics or graphics. Also, a garbage condition does not always indicate that the power-up logic is defective. A problem could exist in RAM, ROM, the video divider chain and of course the CPU itself. Thus, a fault could exist in 75 percent of the computer system.

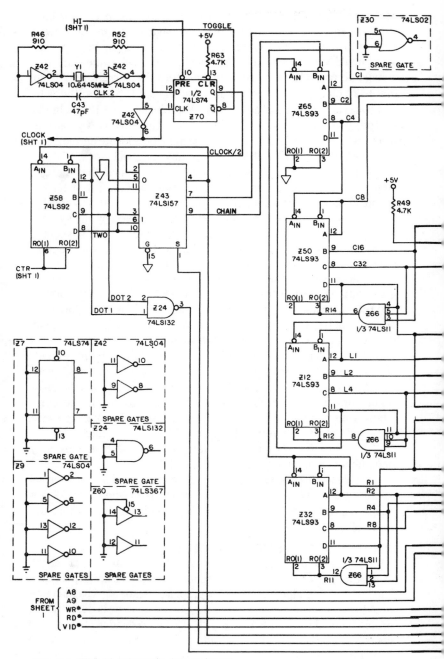

Fig. 9-4. TRS-80 schematic (second part).

246

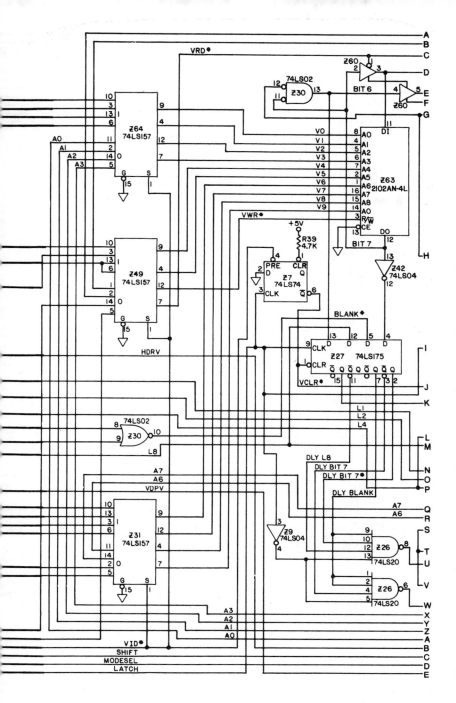

247

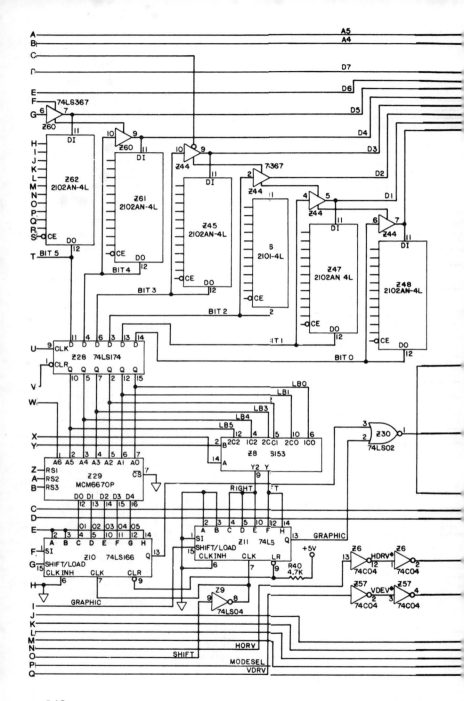

248

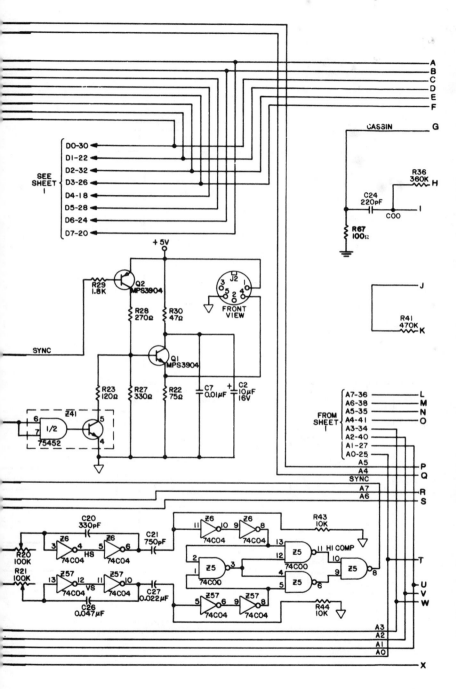

249

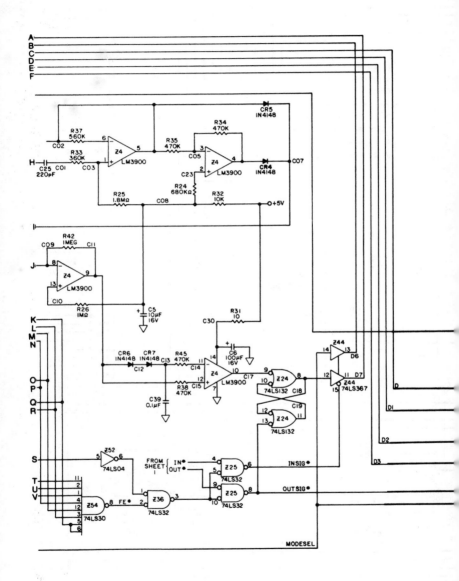

250

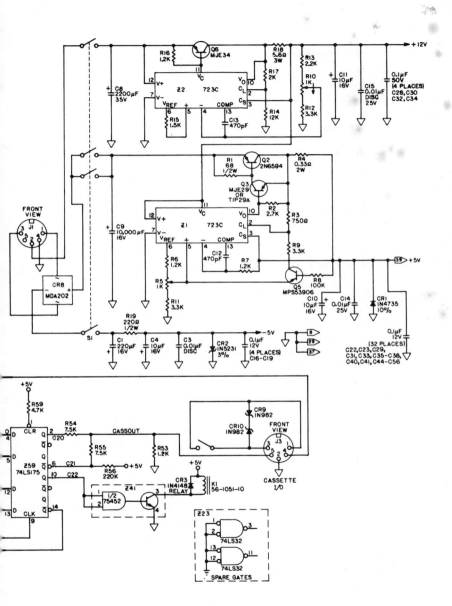

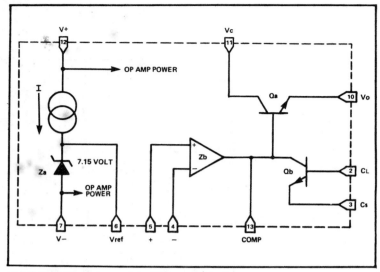

Fig. 9-5. Block diagram of the 723 regulator Z2.

You could start by replacing all of the RAMs, ROMs and the CPU but this would be a waste of time. If the problem was a cold solder connection or a short, replacing all plug-in devices would not solve the problem. The section-isolation technique will probably yield much more positive results. This is based on a removal technique that eliminates sections from the suspect list.

Section Isolation Flowchart

Referring to Fig. 9-6, you will find a flow chart of section-isolation by part removal. Start this process in the parallelogram, block 1, which gives the basic problem. Block 2 instructs you to disassemble the unit and reconnect the video and power inputs. Block 3 is a decision block. Do you have garbage on the screen now? If so, you continue to block 5. If not block 4 tells you to suspect a shorting interconnect cable between the keyboard and the CPU board. You could also have loosened a solder ball during disassembly, and the short is now gone. Examine the interconnect cable carefully for shorting conductors. Also, note any loose solder or wire bits on the board. You may have solved the computer problem just by taking it apart, so run another test.

At block 5, you will turn off power to the unit, wait about ten seconds and then switch the power back on. The delay gives the initialization logic time to reset. If there is now a READY on the

252

screen at block 6, you may have a problem around S2 or C42, as block 7 instructs.

In block 8, you are instructed to remove the DIP shunt (X71) at Z71. Refer to the diagrams in Figs. 9-3 and 9-4. With X71 removed, the RAMs are not electronically in the system. When power is applied, the ROM and the CPU are in communication, but there is no data flow to or from RAM. The screen should show a pattern of 16 character lines of 32 colons. If the CPU shows large colons, you could have RAM or keyboard-type problems. Blocks 11 through 15 will help in isolating that type of problem. As blocks 12 and 14 imply, there are two colon displays. One display is stable. The other is blinking and flickering as the CPU constantly interrupts video addressing. Depending on the status of the keyboard, you could have data line or keyboard problems.

The next step at block 16 is to remove the ROMs. The CPU is now locked up without instruction from ROM. The pattern to look for is a screen full of @ 9s. The display should be in 64-character format at this time. The display will continually flicker.

If you get @ 9s on the screen, you probably have a ROM error. If no @ 9s or partical @ 9s are visible, you could have video chain or video RAM problems. If you still get garbage, maybe the PUC is dead or something is making the CPU not function.

Table 9-1. Power Supply Voltages for Z1 and Z2.

Z1		Z2	
Pin Number	Voltage	Pin Number	Voltage
1	0.00	1	0.00
2	5.30	2	10.60
3	5.00	3	11.99
4	5.00	4	6.92
5	5.00	5	6.92
6	7.46	6	6.92
7	0.00	7	0.00
8	0.00	8	0.00
9	0.33	9	5.72
10	5.89	10	12.31
11	11.99	11	21.16
12	11.99	12	21.69
13	7.05	13	13.48
14	0.00	14	0.00

All voltages are measured with a digital voltmeter. Voltages are referenced to ground at the right side of capacitor C9.

As we see, the part removal isolation technique uses a lot of maybe's, question marks and could be's. The what if's are trying to tell us what section could be at fault. You could have ROM problems and yet get large colons. You could get @ 9s and still have CPU error. But this technique is better than nothing, and the process does give you a starting point.

SIGNAL CONDITION

Normal troubleshooting techniques call for an output-to-input sweep of the bad signal line. Hence, once a bad signal is found, the circuit is traced backward until the signal is correct. The failed device will be located between the good input and bad output.

Activity is defined as any logic transition from high to low or vice versa. For example, the output of oscillator buffer Z42, pin 6, always has activity. There is a constant ouput pulse train at this pin. The signal swings from almost ground to over 3 volts continually.

Steady State is defined as a logic 1 or logic 0. For example, Z40 pin 16, has a steady state logic 1. It is held high by resistor R50. Another example is the logic 0 at pins 6 and 7 of Z56, the CPU clock divider. Z42, pin 8, is always low unless resistor R67 is grounded.

Floating is defined as a signal level between the steady state of a logic 0 and a logic 1. The CPU, the ROMs, the RAMS and the data and address buffers are all tri-stable devices. When tri-state devices are disabled or unselected, the output may show a floating condition. In a floating condition, the output will show system noise flickering through it. The average level of the noise will attain a voltage of 1.5 volts or so. TTL devices define a logic 0 to be equal to, or less than, 0.8 volts. A logic 1 has a voltage equal to, or more than 2.4 volts. Any voltage between these two levels will be considered floating.

CPU PROBLEMS

A problem with the CPU does not mean that Z40 is inoperative. It could indicate you have trouble with the address and data buffers, the control groups, CAS/RAS timing, or with one of the support devices of the CPU. If you suspect a problem with these devices, try substituting a known good CPU for Z40 as a quick check. The flowchart, shown in Fig. 9-7 will help you for CPU troubleshooting.

The primary objective of this chart is to help you quickly find a signal that should be active but is not. The main flow of the chart is on the left side of the blocks. Here, you are checking for activity on address and data lines. With no activity on the address lines, you are

254

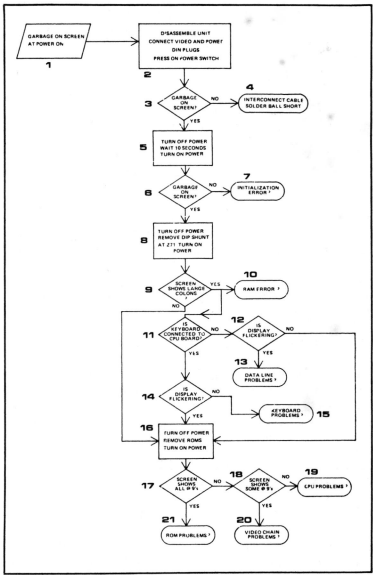

Fig. 9-6. Section isolation flowchart.

immediately branched off to the support group of the CPU to find out why. Pay particular attention to the appearance of address line outputs. Any tri-state looking signal could mean a potential short between address lines. The opposite is true of data lines. These signals may be active and have floating components between active states. Hence, data line shorts are extremely difficult to find, by using an oscilloscope.

ADDRESSING PROBLEMS

Addressing problems are usually associated with open or shorted address lines going to the ROM sockets. Early versions of the boards may have jumper modifications on the solder side that may have broken loose. There is also the chance that vibration has jarred a ROM partially out of its socket. The address lines should be checked at the chip. Normally, there will be activity on all lines.

There are two types of data problems. The first one is the nonrepairable bit error internal to the ROM. The checks contained in the SCQATS program can readily verify this. SCQATS is a special machine language test and debugging tape available from Radio Shack for the TRS-80. If the ROM problem is too severe for SCQATS loading, a replacement test may be required. The second type of data problem is the short or open on the data output. If you remove DIP shunt Z3, the ROMs will tri-state and you can check for a floating state on the data pins.

RAM PROBLEMS

RAM problems are slightly more difficult to troubleshoot because of multiplexing of the address inputs. Aside from an addressing difference, the RAMs are checked like the ROMS. If you have a RAM problem and the system will not load SCQATS, you can replace the eight RAMs with a known good set. If this clears the faults, start replacing your standard RAMs with the ones you took out, one by one. Power up after each exchange to see if you still have a READY. Continue this process until you have isolated the defective RAMs.

ADDRESS DECODER TIPS

A problem in the address decoder section will probably point you in the memory direction. For example, if the ROM is never addressed with ROM, you would think you have ROM problems. Thus, if you suspect one of the memory locations, keep in mind that the address decoder sources the memory selects. The select inputs to the different memories should be the very first thing to check out.

Since the address decoder is made up of gates, it should be easy to repair once you locate the fault. The hard part is knowing when to suspect a fault with the decoder section. Section isolation

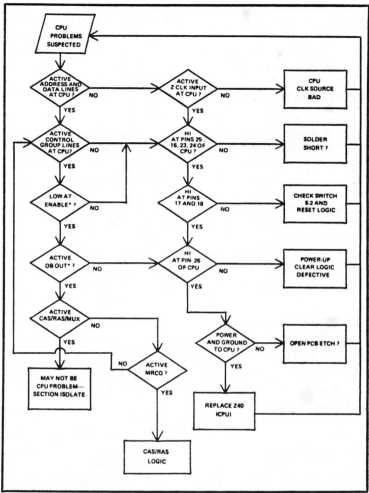

Fig. 9-7. CPU flowchart.

demands that the address decoder be functional, or at least partially. Unfortunately, there is no cut and dry way to determine if this section is operating correctly. Of course, you can monitor each output to see if it's responding, but you really cannot be sure the signal is supposed to be there when it is.

KEYBOARD INFORMATION

Difficulty with the keyboard is usually mechanical. Sticking keycaps, bouncy keys and broken interconnect cables are common.

Shorts in the keyboard matrix are usually easy to detect. If you find an alphanumeric character displayed right after the >, that particular key or PCB run may be shorted. A completely dead keyboard could be caused by lack of power, a broken interconnect cable. Also, the address decoder is not feeding a signal to the keyboard.

THE VIDEO DIVIDER CHAIN

Problems in the video divider chain will usually be associated with the stability of the display. Loss of vertical or horizontal reference frequencies can sometimes be traced back to defective counters on bad reset gates. Because the master clock/oscillator of the system is included in this section, inactive (dead) system troubleshooting can end up here.

Since most of the reference and timing signals for the video processor are generated in the divider chain, most—but not all—display difficulties can be isolated to this section. This is especially true of vertical roll or horizontal tear of the display. If the horizontal or vertical reference frequency is not getting to the sync processors, the problem definitely is a divider chain foulup.

THE VIDEO RAM

If you suspect video RAM problems, you should try a SCQATS tape test loading. SCQATS will be most helpful in rooting out bit error in the RAMs. If the test generates large amounts of bit errors, you should suspect either the divider chain or the video RAM addressing multiplexer.

Normally, addressing errors occur when there is a short or open between the multiplexer and the RAMs. Signal activity on the address inputs of the RAMs can be easily checked with an oscilloscope. All address lines (VO through V9) should be active in 64-character format. There will not normally be any floating conditions on these inputs. The logic input to the video RAM will only be active during a CPU data transfer. Normally, it should be high.

VIDEO PROCESSING PROBLEMS

Problems in the video processing section can range anywhere from a blank screen to missing dots. Usually, the fault is easily found because this section is a serial type. For example, if you have graphics problems, you know there are only two chips that are used as graphics handling devices. You should then look around shift register Z11 and graphics generator Z8. The parts that are strictly alphanumeric are character generator Z29 and its shift register Z10. Defective devices that can affect both alphanumeric and graphics are Z26, Z27, Z30 and the video mixing circuits, consisting of Q1 and Q2.

SYNC GENERATOR SERVICE POINTS

The sync generator section is one of the easiest circuits to troubleshoot. If the timing reference is getting to Z6 and Z57, it is a simple process to find the point where you have lost the signal. A problem can occur with the adjust pots, R20 or R21. Severe heat buildups may cause these parts to fail. Capacitors C20 and C26 are usually dependable unless they are physically damaged. You may find C21 or C27 shorted. These capacitors are mylar and are very suspectible to shorting out under impact stress.

An important point about this circuit is that Z6 and Z57 are CMOS devices. Unlike TTL, they are high-impedance devices that consume little current. A floating condition on a CMOS input will not necessarily give a floating display on an oscilloscope. A floating condition may look high or low depending on the charge of the broken line tied to the input point. Even the resistance of your finger across a broken run can complete the circuit and cause a CMOS device to operate. When you remove your finger from the run or pin, circuit operation may fade away very slowly as the PC board run discharges.

Chapter 10
Troubleshooting
Microprocessor Systems

The troubleshooting philosophy for microprocessor-based devices is generally no different than for any other types of digital systems. As with any circuit you are trying to analyze or troubleshoot, it is helpful to first become familiar with the circuit. Studying the theory of operation, the block diagrams and the schematic provides a basic understanding from which to work. In this chapter, problems relating to microprocessor systems and the troubleshooting techniques for dealing with them will be discussed.

A number of testing problems are unique to microprocessor systems. For one thing, most of the control is in the software, so that signal flow is hard to trace. Another difficulty is that everything happens too rapidly to see in real time. In most cases, a microprocessor system, unlike many logic circuits, cannot be stopped and manipulated. Measurements must be taken while the microprocessor is running. Thus to troubleshoot the micros use the oscilloscope, signature analyzer and logic analyzer as these instruments rely on circuit activity for their measurements. A scope such as the HP-model 1742A shown in Fig. 10-1 will help you identify micro system problems.

Microprocessor bus structure poses additional difficulties. Data on these buses are often unstable or meaningless because of three-state outputs, multiplexing and switching transients. These conditions cause no problems for the system itself, since it is synchronous and knows when the bus lines contain stable signals. The signature analyzer and the logic analyzer also know when these

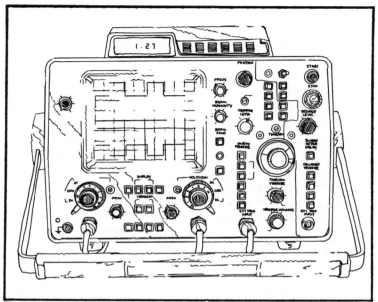

Fig. 10-1. A Hewlett-Packard model 1742A oscilloscope used to troubleshoot microprocessor systems.

lines are valid, because of the clock signals provided to them. The scope does not have this capability. It provides little quantitative information, but is useful for examining qualitative factors, such as general activity, logic levels, waveform timing and bus conflicts.

Because bus structures also make it possible for many devices to be connected together on a single node, finding the one bad device on such a node can be difficult. The current tracer is useful for this purpose. The data bus also acts as a digital signal feedback path and tends to propagate errors through good circuits and then back to the fault source. The best way to deal with this problem is to open the feedback path when possible. We will be looking at a few of these techniques.

Complex devices are often connected to the microprocessor buses. It is difficult to test these devices using simple stimulus-response testing. The correct operation of these devices can be verified by swapping them with a known good chip, or by observing that the function they perform for the system is being performed correctly.

Microprocessors are sequential machines. Program flow depends on a long sequence of instructions and events. If even a single bit of information is incorrect, the whole system can go awry. Noise glitches and bad memory bits are the most common sources of single-bit errors. Others will also be discussed later. These failures are difficult to pinpoint because the entire system may appear to be operating incorrectly.

CLOCKS

Bad clocks can cause fouled, but running, systems. A number of malfunctions can result in system clocking problems. Clock problems can show up as a failure of the system to function at all (no activity), the ability to function only open-loop (free-running), or semi-functional activity (a meaningless and undefined program sequence). Some microprocessors are sensitive to clock speed. Because many systems run at spec, even a small variation in clock rate (too fast) can cause system failures. If the system runs too slow, dynamic storage cells on ICs in the system may fail. Both of these problems are more likely to occur when resistor and capacitor (RC) clock circuits are used instead of the more accurate and stable crystal-controlled circuits. However, crystals can sometime break into a third overtone oscillation mode, causing a much higher than expected clock rate. In addition, clock voltage levels are not necessarily TTL compatible, but may be much wider in voltage swing. Microprocessor clock specs can be found on the device data sheets and can be checked using frequency counters and oscilloscope.

POWER-UP RESET

The power-up reset circuit of the microprocessor can also cause fouled, but running, system operation. A reset pulse that is nonexistent, too short, too noisy or too slow in transition can start everything off at the wrong time, resulting in out-of-sequence, partial, or no reset activity. Problems can also occur in reset circuits that are susceptible to power-supply glitches. Even when Schmitt input circuits are used, slow edges can cause reset timing skew from one device to another within some systems. This will cause some of the devices to power up before the others, resulting in erroneous behavior. A too rapid on-off-on system power sequence will fail to restart many systems. It may then be necessary to increase the off time to allow the power supplies and restart circuits to discharge.

None of these restart failures will necessarily prevent the system from running. It may run for a short time and then stop, lock up in meaningless program loop, or even perform most of its normal operations. The key point to remember is that the system must complete the power-up reset sequence to insure that all of the test, control and initialization operations necessary to bring the system up have been performed.

Power-up reset circuits are normally operative only when the system is initially powered up. They can also be monitored at that time with storage oscilloscopes and logic analyzers. They can also be manually overdriven and controlled externally for testing purposes.

INTERRUPTS

Stuck or noisy interrupt lines can cause faulty system operation. The system may work with a stuck line but it will do so very slowly (spending most of its time servicing the "phantom" interrupt). Noisy interrupt lines can cause sporadic system changes to occur (e.g., a phantom depression). Or peripheral inputs or outputs may occur at improper times. Sometimes the system may not respond at all to certain I/O devices, which may occur when a higher priority interrupt has disabled the lower ones.

Interrupt line activity can be monitored with a logic probe, logic analyzer, or oscilloscope. Interrupts are asynchronous in nature and can be manually controlled (enabled or disabled) for testing purposes.

SIGNAL DEGRADATION

The long parallel bus and control lines present in medium-to-large microprocessor systems are sometimes susceptible to crosstalk and transmission line problems on critical lines (such as clocks and enables). These problems can show up as glitches on adjacent signal lines or ringing on the driving line (causing multiple transitions through a logic threshold). Either of these situations can reject faulty data or control signals that are very difficult to detect. This problem is most common when signal lines are too long and already taxing the timing margins of the system. When extender cards are added to these systems or high-humidity conditions exist, failures may occur. Cross-coupling of lines on extender cards can be a problem when fast signal transition lines (such as Schottky gate outputs) run alongside other signal lines, even when they are on opposite sides of a PC board.

MEMORY SYSTEM CHECKS

Memory failures in microprocessor systems can produce deviant system behavior in a number of ways. Anything from a total system failure to a single faulty bit of stored data can occur. Most memory failures can be found during the power-up self-test program, unless the memory failure prevents this program from running. If the system does not do a RAM verification test and no RAM test service fixtures or procedures are provided, it is nearly impossible to test the RAM. You will probably need to resort to substitution techniques when a RAM becomes suspect.

RAM failures occurring in the area of the memory used for the stack will usually cause the system to crash, even for a single-bit error. Otherwise, RAM failures may cause soft errors that result in unreliable system operation. Faulty dynamic RAM refresh circuitry is another factor to consider in diagnosing apparent RAM failures.

ROMs can also fail. Such failures are more frequent when nonmask programmable types are used. A single bad bit could crash the system. Even worse, 99 percent of it could work and 1 percent could produce erroneous results. ROMs can be effectively tested during power-up self-test, if such tests are designed in. But unlike RAMs, ROMs can also be tested by other techniques if no self-test is provided. One such technique involves free-running the system and then using a signature analyzer to either verify documented signatures or compare the outputs of a suspected ROM with that of a ROM in a known good system. Figure 10-2 shows the H-P Signature analyzer being used in such a check.

USING SELF-TEST PROGRAMS

The programmability of microprocessor-base systems can be used to great advantage for system testing. Programs stored in the ROM of the system can test ROMs, RAMs and the processor itself. Often the I/O can be tested to some extent. Software can also be used to provide stimulus to an external test instrument, such as an signature snalyzer.

ROM TESTING

The most common technique for testing ROMs uses a checksum. When the ROM is programmed, all of its words are added together, ignoring any carries that result. This number is complemented and stored in the last (or sometimes the first) word of the ROM, so that when all the words are added together (including the checksum stored in the last or first byte), the result is zero. If the total is not zero at the end of the test sequence, then something is wrong with the ROM.

Unfortunately, the checksum is not totally reliable. It detects any single-bit errors; however, there are many combinations of two

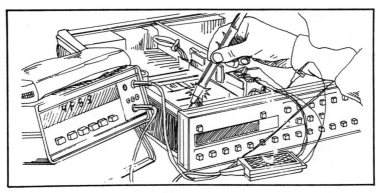

Fig. 10-2. Hewlett-Packard Signature analyzer in action.

or more errors that still produce the correct checksum. Thus, a ROM that passes a checksum test is probably good. If the test fails, something is definitely wrong, though it might not be the ROM itself.

RAM TESTING

RAMs are tested by writing a pattern into the memory, reading it back and verifying that it is unchanged. Of the many different patterns that can be used, a common one is the checkerboard. In this pattern, all the bits are set to alternating ones and zeros. Once all memory locations have been tested, the pattern is repeated with each bit reversed, verifying that each bit of the RAM can store a one and a zero. Many other patterns used to test RAMs are specifically aimed at detecting various failure mechanisms within the RAM.

No memory test can guarantee 100-percent accuracy, even though it may show that each bit can store a one or a zero. RAMs can be pattern sensitive. For example, one location might correctly store 01010101 and 10101010 but fail when 01111000 is stored. Even for a small RAM, it would take an extremely long time to test every possible pattern sequence. For this reason, RAM test credibility is generally much lower than that of ROMs. As with the checksum test, if a RAM passes the system self-test program, it is probably good. If it fails the test, something is definitely wrong.

MULTIPLEXED I/O

Multiplexed keyboards and displays often share some of the same scanning circuits. In these situations a struck key can appear to make the display fail. Likewise, a bad display driver input could cause a keyboard error. The interaction between common scan circuits must be considered in making diagnosis.

INTERFACES

Many microprocessor systems interface with other systems through external communication lines (RS-232C, telephone modem, etc.). These lines are frequently long and are often exposed to sources of electrical interference, such as relays, transformers, motors and lightning surges. Electromagnetic interference (EMI) coming from these sources can cause the transmission of faulty data, overstressing of interface circuits, and with lightning a complete component failure. Generally, output line driver circuits tend to have higher-than-average failure rates, due both to EMI stressing and to the high transition currents that result from driving capacitive interfacing cables.

TROUBLESHOOTING TREES

A troubleshooting tree is a graphical means of showing the sequence of tests performed on a product under test. These trees are often drawn as flowcharts in which the results of each test determine what step for repairing microprocessor-based devices can save considerable time and effort.

Shown in Fig. 10-3 is a portion of the troubleshooting tree for a digital voltmeter. Theoretically, it should lead you to the defect by means of actions and decisions taken along the tree. This may not always be the case. A perfect troubleshooting tree must consider all possible failures, a difficult task for the person writing the troubleshooting tree to meet. Also, these trees tend to be fairly generalized, lacking the specifics desired for making tests and decisions. Few troubleshooting trees provide practical information about how a specified test or measurement relates to what the circuit does or is supposed to do. If the troubleshooting tree fails to direct you to the actual fault, you can be left at a dead end. However, the tree will often be your best guide—at least to begin with.

The good tree seldom leads to a dead end and provides a logical, well-directed sequence of tests and measurements, requiring a minimum level of understanding of the circuit under test. Often good trees include advanced techniques such as signature analysis to simplify the procedure. In troubleshooting a device, even the poorer troubleshooting trees can be useful for localizing a failure area in the system and can save time.

Now let's take a look at some general steps that you can take to troubleshoot a microprocessor-based product. Numerous service techniques and "tricks of the trade" are interspersed with the description.

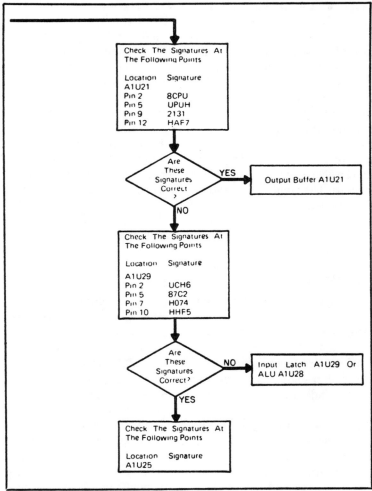

Fig. 10-3. Typical troubleshooting tree.

NOTE THE PROBLEM

It is important to have a general understanding of the defective unit so that you can be sure that a problem really exists. To some degree, you should know what it does and how it operates. Microprocessors allow designers to design systems that are not only complex in function, but sometimes complex to operate as well. Be sure the apparent problem is not a user error, but a real device fault. Few things are more frustrating than trying to repair something that is not faulty. In some situations, it appears that a device should do something it was not actually designed to do. For example, a DVM AC SELECT switch may work on VOLTS but not on AMPS. This design limitation can usually be verified in the operating manual and does not indicate a product fault, but only a shortcoming.

Design bugs in the firmware (ROM) can sometimes cause failures when used under conditions that were not anticipated during the product design. These are more likely to occur in early production runs and can best be verified (if suspected) by checking with the manufacturer. At the other extreme, a problem may actually exist but not show up because the devise was not properly operated. These kinds of problems are often very simple to detect, but can also be very complex. For example, errors can occur when an unusual sequence of operations is performed. Because the complex problems are much more difficult to test for, extensive test procedures are used to test units at the factory. The customer, bringing in a unit for repair, has no trouble pointing out a problem, but it is up to the technician to solve it.

THE FRONT PANEL

A great deal of diagnostic information can often be obtained without removing the unit from its case. Most microprocessor-based systems have a front panel. Usually there are switches, LEDs and indicators plus inputs and outputs. Checking the front panel is a process in which the switches, buttons and other inputs are used to solicit responses from the device that can be observed using its indicators and other outputs. For instance, if the indicators are all dead when the power is turned on, you might suspect a bad switch, fuse, power cord, battery connection or the power supply. If one segment of a display is out, it is probably the display itself or the driver circuit.

Always take advantage of any designed-in-performance verification or power-up test modes and diagnostic messages that are available. At this point you may have some idea of where the problem is or you may already have the unit repaired. But in all likelihood, neither has taken place.

CHECK THE MANUAL

If all else fails, look at the service information. This poor (but prevalent) attitude makes even less sense for microprocessor-based devices than for conventional electronic ones. There may be many tips of service aids and procedures in the manual just waiting for you to check out. Special service switches, jumpers, test devices, indicators and test techniques can make the task much easier.

Try to understand the circuits and figure out where things are. Check out the theory of operation section, the block diagrams and the schematics. You don't have to do this in great detail but just enough to have some idea of what is going on. Identify the microprocessor, ROM, RAM, I/O, address-decoder, clock, bus, control and interrupt portions of the system.

The life of an IC is generally a sequence of predictable events. It is born in the IC plant and is shipped to a product manufacturer. There it is inserted into a circuit board, which in turn is inserted into the finished product. Then the product goes into service, and the IC remains there for the rest of its useful life. Needless to say, not all ICs live a long and good life.

TYPES OF FAILURES

Common fault sources and the best troubleshooting techniques for finding them depend on the history of the product and the environment in which it is tested. When a new product is first turned on at the plant, almost anything could be wrong. Products that fail in the field have all worked at one time. Assembly errors, such as wrong components and miswired circuits, usually need not be considered in the field. Also, the likelihood of solder shorts and multiple faults in much greater on the production line than out in the field. Actual in-service failures are usually caused by components or connections that have failed.

CHECKING THE EASY THINGS FIRST

It makes good sense to look at the items that can be tested and repaired easily. The simple things are as likely to fail as the more complicated ones. A case in point is the power supply: It is actually one of the more failure-prone portions of most electronic systems. It is also one of the easiest to test and troubleshoot. Out-of-spec voltages can cause erratic circuit performance. If the voltage is not checked first, it could take considerable time to pinpoint the problem. A mechanical inspection can also be fruitful. Poor PC board and cable connections, broken wires and loose parts can usually be found either visually or by touch.

COMMON PRODUCTION-LINE TROUBLESHOOTING PROBLEMS

A number of common sources of failure in a manufacturing environment can be found through careful visual inspection of circuit assemblies. It is easy to check for improperly set switches and jumpers, wrong components or right ones put in backward, and cold solder joints. Backward resistor packs can be tough to locate electrically because they can cause interaction between unrelated logic nodes, but they are easy to check visually.

Two of the more common failures in production are solder and gold or copper shorts on printed circuit boards. These can usually be removed with a sharp knife. When the precise place of the short is not known, there is a rather novel technique for removing it that often works. The procedure involves charging a 100,000 μF (or larger) capacitor to 5 volts, as this would be safe for logic circuits. Then, with the cables solidly connected to the two shorted nodes and proper polarity observed, discharge the capacitor into them and listen for a snapping sound on the board. Check continuity to see if the short has been opened and, if not, try again. This technique should be used with caution since it will open the weakest link of the current path, which may not be the circuit short, but a fine-trace PC pattern.

A relatively new problem in production is the occurrence of bent IC pins caused by automatic component insertion machines. This can result in an open electrical connection between the IC and the PC board, an intermittent connection, or shorts to traces near or under the IC. The bent pin is often difficult to spot visually because it may look as though it is properly soldered in place. The best way to tell this is to look at the bottom of the board for the ends of any IC pins or along the plane of the board to see under the ICs.

PC board edge connectors are commonly used. They may cause problems in production when their borders are cut off center or when they are accidently covered with solder resist or board-sealing spray. Visual inspection can reveal such problems.

Wire-wrap boards are prone to bent posts that can cause shorting. Other common production problems include 14-pin ICs placed in the wrong end of a 16-pin socket, miswiring, wire shorts between pins and signal coupling (crosstalk) due to closely bundled wires.

Visual inspection of a device that fails in the field can reveal such things as loose wires, broken traces and dirty connectors. A tap on the right spot of the cabinet can be used to detect loose or intermittent connections and stuck relays. Stressing boards and connectors (by twisting and flexing) can often help to locate some of these problems. You might suspect the PC board edge connectors when a unit is dead on arrival. You may want to try reseating all of the assemblies and circuit board connections to determine whether the problem is poor connector contact. A pencil eraser is useful for cleaning dirty edge connectors.

BOARD SWAPPING

If any of the PC boards are easy to remove and replace with known good ones, you can try swapping them. Boards may also be swapped out of the same type equipment for a quick test. The risk in board swapping is that you could damage a good board because of the same electrical overload that damaged the defective one when it was installed. In any case, power to the unit should be turned off when removing or installing boards or assemblies.

If an identical product is available, functional comparisons can sometimes be informative. This comparison can be especially useful in situations in which it is not clear that there is actually a hardware problem (it may be a product idiosyncrasy or design limitation).

If a device in a socket is suspect, try tapping it first to see if there is a loose connection and then try subbing in a known good one. Note, however, that one of the *last* devices you should suspect, but is most often replaced first, is the microprocessor chip. The actual failure test rate for these chips is very low. However, because they are complex and their correct operation is difficult to verify, they are often replaced right from the start. This usually applies to the LSI chips used with the micros.

STRESS TESTING TECHNIQUE

A technique called stress testing can be very effective in dealing with marginal or intermittent failures. Stress testing can often cause these types of faults to temporarily improve or become worse, thus helping in pinpointing the fault. Boards are stressed physically by tapping or twisting them, thermally by heat (heat gun) or by cooling them (freeze spray) and electrically by varying the supply voltage. Thermal stressing can be used to isolate a fault in a specific device on a board very precisely because heat or cold can be applied to a single suspected component. Intermittents can result from marginal chips, lead bonds, solder joints, connections and drive and timing circuits.

Briefly touching each device on a circuit board can pinpoint a component that is operating too hot. When a particular device runs a good-bit hotter than others of the same type, a problem may exist. A faulty device can sometimes be hot enough to burn your finger, so use this technique with caution. Best to use a temperature probe for these checks. Be aware also that some good components may run hotter than you expect during normal operation, and that the temperatures may vary widely from one device to another.

POWER SUPPLY SHORTS

There are some effective ways of dealing with shorts across the power supply. The first thing to do in a multiboard system is to try to localize the short on a single board. This can be done by removing one board at a time until the short disappears, which indicates the shorted one.

One technique for finding the short on a faulty board is to inject current through the two shorted lines with the logic pulser while the power is off. The current tracer is then used to follow this current to the short. Keep in mind that capacitors, especially electrolytics, will have some current going into them because of the pulsing current. Shorted capacitors can be found by using the current tracer to compare the current levels going into identical capacitors on the same board. The capacitor that shows a much higher level than the others is likely to be shorted. This technique is particularly useful for finding shorted ceramic bypass capacitors.

Another technique for locating power bus shorts is to feed a relatively high current (about 3 to 5 amps) into the short. Be sure to maintain the same voltage polarity and not to exceed the supply voltage normally present. The current path to the short can often be determined by using a DVM with a high resolution (0.01 mV) to look at voltage drops on the power bus traces. Voltages are developed across the traces that are in the path going to the short, and not anywhere else. Refer to Fig. 10-4.

A less scientific, but much more dramatic, technique for finding power bus shorts is to freeze the entire board, allow moisture to condense on it and then power it up with a 3 to 5 amp supply. As it warms up and defrosts, the current path becomes visible and, in many cases, will pinpoint the location of the short.

HOW TO ISOLATE THE FAULT

Once the easy things have been tried unsuccessfully, it is time to get down to the "nitty gritty." At this point, individual troubleshooting skills, intuition and knowledge of the product can really make the difference.

First, be sure to take advantage of any designed-in and documented circuit isolation features, such as selected board removal, service jumpers and special test modes and procedures. It

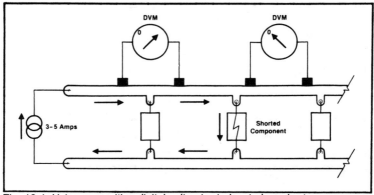

Fig. 10-4. Using a sensitive digital voltmeter to locate bus short.

can be very useful to separate the microprocessor system from the peripheral circuits to allow you to diagnose each portion independently.

An important troubleshooting concept is half-splitting. Although the term may be new to you, you have been using the process for many years. It is also known as divide and conquer. This technique involves choosing a point roughly in the middle of the circuit. It is just as likely that a fault exists before as after this midpoint. If the performance is correct up to that point, the problem will be after the midpoint. This process works best in circuits that have clear, unidirectional signal paths without large feedback loops. Even with microprocessor-based systems, this approach can be effective because the circuits outside the microprocessor portion often fit these guidelines.

DIGITAL FAILURE MODES

When suspicion falls on the digital portion, the first thing to look for is signal activity. With a logic probe you can examine activity of the clock signals, bus lines, chip enables and control lines. Absence of activity on any of these nodes indicates a possible problem.

The most common failure modes for digital ICs is open lead bonds inside the package. These are thin wires conecting the package pins to the IC chip. If an output lead bond opens, the output pin floats and the logic probe will probably indicate a constant floating logic level because of other device inputs connected to the node. If an input lead bond opens, one or more of the IC outputs will usually appear to malfunction (stuck high, low, or executing its logic function incorrectly). If any of these outputs goes to a three-state

273

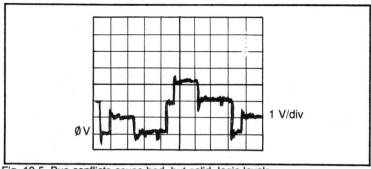

Fig. 10-5. Bus conflicts cause bad, but solid, logic levels.

bus, it can cause bus conflicts (more than one output at a time), and the current tracer can be used to find these. Bus conflicts are often observed on an oscilloscope by the presence of bad, but solid, logic levels on the bus lines. However, as shown in Fig. 10-5, the scope provides no information as to the source of the fault. Good bus lines can appear to have solid, bad levels present when all devices on the bus are off.

Another common digital IC failure is a shorted input pin to ground. This fault is often caused by a bad input protection diode on the chip. It usually appears as a stuck low level, which can be seen with the logic probe. An oscilloscope connected to a node with this type of problem shows a voltage level near ground being pulled up, perhaps a few hundred millivolts, whenever a logic 1 ouput on that node turns on (See Fig. 10-6).

The current tracer provides an excellent means of pinpointing shorted input pins. If a current tracer is not available, another means for locating stuck inputs and outputs involves the use of a sensitive (high resolution) DVM and a can of freeze spray. Connect the DVM to the stuck node and select the most sensitive DC voltage range available. Then, while monitoring the voltage, spray each IC connected to the stuck node—one at a time—to change its temperature. Any noticeable change in voltage (more than 10 mV) on the node indicates that the IC being sprayed is drawing current. A heat source can be used in the same way. This technique relies on the properties of the semiconductor used in the IC that relates voltage to temperature.

ISOLATION TECHNIQUES

Once a particular input or output pin is suspected, it is useful to isolate it from the rest of the circuit. A quick, nondestructive way to

274

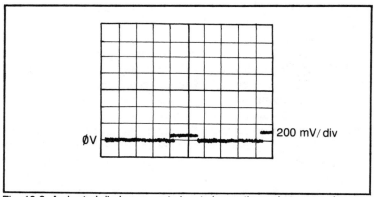
Fig. 10-6. A shorted diode on a gate input clamps the node to ground.

do so is to suck the solder away from the area between the pins and the PC board pad, using a vacuum desoldering tool or solder wicking braid. Then bend the pin so that it is centered in the hole of the pad, not touching at any point. Use a continuity tester to verify that the pin is no longer in electrical contact with the board.

An extender board with switches on bus and signal lines can be used to break selected signals between a PC board and the rest of the system. In this manner, feedback paths and stuck buses can be removed from the main system. An even simpler way to open selected signals going through a board edge connector is to place a piece of tape on the PC board edge fingers that you wish to isolate.

A somewhat unconventional, but often effective means of detecting bus line problems, is to measure the resistance to ground

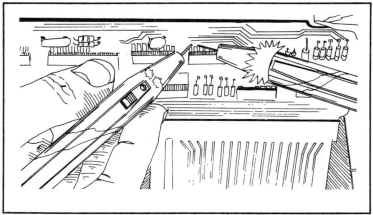
Fig. 10-7. A Hewlett-Packard 546A logic pulser probe in use.

(with the power off) of each of the lines in a particular bus. The resistance of each of these lines is usually the same. If any differs substantially, you may suspect a problem on this line. If two lines show the same (lower) resistance, the two lines may be shorted together. In either case, check the diagram to see if the arrangement of circuits connected to these lines could explain the difference before going any further.

Overriding interrupt lines and chip enable pins on suspected devices can be used to verify that the IC is functioning correctly. This can be done by momentarily shorting the appropriate pin high or low, or by using a logic pulser. A logic pulser probe is shown being used in Fig. 10-7.

FEEDBACK LOOPS

Digital feedback loops are often difficult to troubleshoot because errors propagate around and around. A feedback loop with a faulty output signal sends this signal back to the input to produce more bad outputs. Opening this feedback path prevents the faulty output signals from going back to the input. Then, if controlled inputs to the loop can be generated, the signal flow from the input to the output can be observed. Often, however, it is not easy to provide this input (many lines may need to be controlled). It may also be difficult to predict correct circuit operation. If another working device or board of the same circuitry is available, it is sometimes practical to allow the output of the good circuit to control the inputs of both circuits. In this manner, you know that the circuit under test is getting the correct input signal. It is then a matter of comparing the nodes of the two circuits and looking for any differences.

CONCLUSION

No amount of knowledge and experience can totally compensate for inadequate service data and information. In some cases, shotgunning (replacing components until the problem is solved) may be the best way out. However, as shown in Fig. 10-8, this is not always a practical solution. Most microprocessor-based products do not fall into this class. Future products will probably incorporate advanced service techniques, such as signature analysis, as more designers realize that the old troubleshooting methods and tools used for random logic are not very effective in dealing with microprocessors.

Fig. 10-8. Circuit shotgunning can often produce unfavorable results.

Microprocessor systems can be thought of as an extension of traditional digital logic. Many of the components, circuit designs, and troubleshooting tools and techniques are the same. However, there are some differences. Microprocessor systems are bus-structured, and many of the devices on the bus are complex LSI ICs. The signal activity between the devices on the buses is constant and complex. It is often useful to break the data bus, which is the main feedback path of the system, to help isolate a fault that causes the entire system to malfunction.

Although troubleshooting trees provide an orderly approach for locating system faults, they are not always adequate. There are

Fig. 10-9. The INTELLEC Promp 80/85 8080A microcomputer design aid (courtesy of INTEL).

numerous techniques, procedures, and tricks that can be effective in diagnosing, isolating and locating faults in microprocessor-based products. Many of these were discussed in this chapter and all you need-do is put them into action.

The INTEL Promp 80 shown in Fig. 10-9 is a low-cost, fully assembled microcomputer design aid. This device simplifies programming of the system 80 microcomputers, 8080A processors and

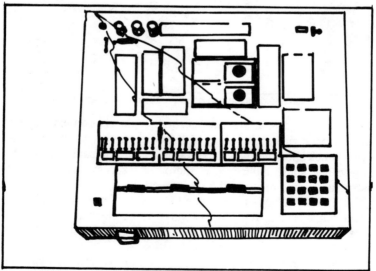

Fig. 10-10. E & L Instruments model MMD-1 microcomputer designer system.

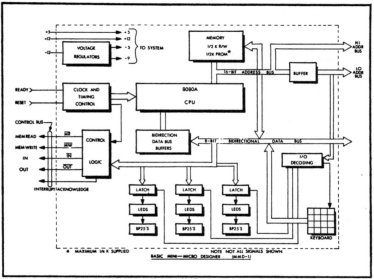

Fig. 10-11. Block diagram of the E & L MMD-1 microcomputer designer system.

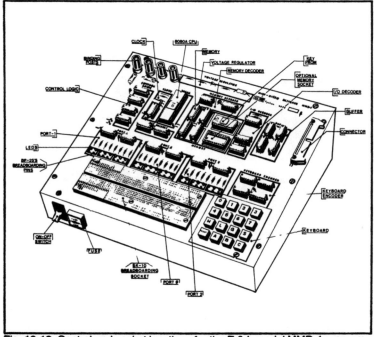

Fig. 10-12. Control and socket locations for the E & L model MMD-1 programmer.

279

I/O devices. The 8080A programs can be entered and debugged with calculator-like ease on the large, informative display and keyboard panel.

Figure 10-10 shows the E & L Instruments model MMD-1 mini-microcomputer designer that lets you easily program the 8080A microprocessor chip. A block diagram of the MMD-1 programmer system is shown in Fig. 10-11. Controls and component locations on the MMD-1 are shown in Fig. 10-12.

Chapter 11
Video Games

Games that people now play on the screens of TV sets are of course well known as video games. These games operate with digital logic pulses that simulate the playing field lines, the game ball and the players instead of the analog video now used for TV station signals. The digital video is added to the vertical sync, horizontal sync and blanking to make up the composite video. This video information modulates an oscillator (rf unit) and is usually on either channel 3 or 4 for TV set operation. The modulated carrier goes through a TV/GAME SELECTOR switch before being fed to the TV antenna terminals. The modulated video game signal operates the TV receiver the same as any TV station or cable channel signal. Thus, any standard TV receiver may be used with no modification necessary. Many of these video games use LSI (large-scale integration) ICs that have hundreds of transistors and diodes which cut down considerably on the required components.

CLOCK CIRCUITS

To operate the video game, a clock generator is needed. The clock generates a square wave signal that is used as a reference for all other circuit systems. The square wave is called the clock signal and is often produced by a multivibrator circuit.

In this chapter we will check out one of Radio Shack's video games and at some troubleshooting information and tips on this unit. Next we will see how the RCA Studio II video game operates and how to use the test cartridge for complete check-out procedures of this system. The chapter concludes with information on the Motorolas MC1372 color TV video modulator chip used in video games, color generator test instruments and video tape recorders.

RADIO SHACK MODEL 60-3051 VIDEO GAME

The Radio Shack TV game is divided into six major subsections. They are the game chip, power supply, video mixer, oscillator, modulator and audio amplifier.

Shown in Fig. 11-1 is a block diagram of the TV game electronics. The power supply provides power to all sections. The game chip develops all video signals and processes the ball and paddle options, as well as receiving game selections from the selector switch. This IC performs all of the game functions. All other sections and components support this main game IC. The crystal oscillator section feeds the master reference frequency of 2.01216 MHz to the game chip. The video mixer section accepts the five video outputs from the game chip and makes one composite waveform that is then fed to the modulator. The modulator, as its name implies, amplitude modulates the video information onto the carrier frequency. This carrier is of the proper frequency so that TV channel 3 or 4 can be used to receive the games. The audio amplifier section current-amplifies the audio generated by the game IC to drive the speaker.

VIDEO GAME TROUBLESHOOTING

The following test equipment is required for video game troubleshooting:

■ Oscilloscope—30 to 50 MHz (triggered) and a low-capacitance (LC) probe.
■ Digital voltmeter (DVM).
■ Frequency counter (optional).

Refer to Fig. 11-2 for a complete schematic of the video game as we look at some troubleshooting information.

Power Supply

If the video game does not operate at all, the power supply would be the prime suspect. Apply 9.0 VDC to the input and check for 6.5 VDC at TP5. If TP5 passes the test, move on to the oscillator circuit. If TP5 fails, check for 7.1 VDC at TP4. If an improper voltage is found, check CR1 and CR2 for proper opera-

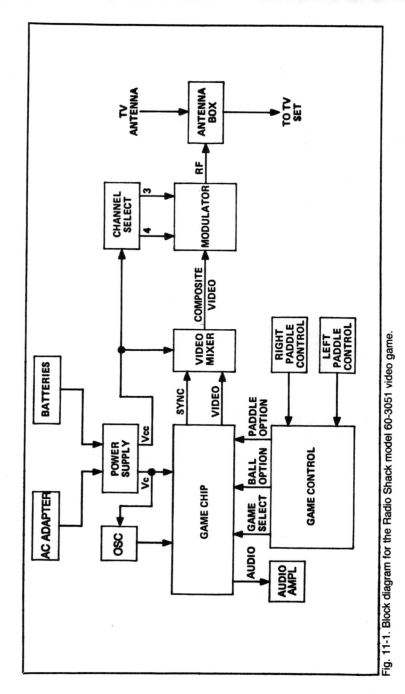

Fig. 11-1. Block diagram for the Radio Shack model 60-3051 video game.

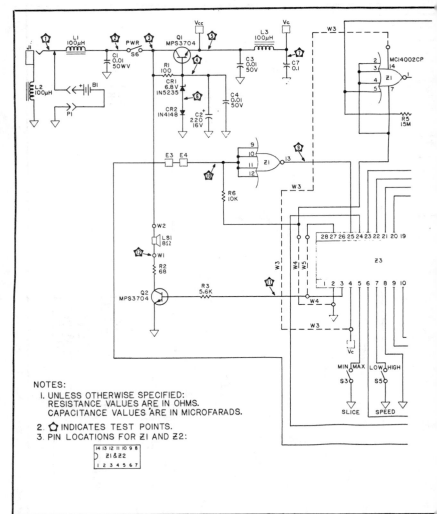

Fig. 11-2. Complete schematic of the Radio Shack model 60-3051 video game.

tion. Also check capacitor C2 for shorts. If TP4 tests good, then Q1 may be defective.

Transistor Q1 will be destroyed (open) if there is a short on the V_{cc} line, even momentarily. If the fault is not found, continue to trace back to TP3 (unregulated power to the audio and regulation section), switch S6, TP2, TP1 and finally to J1.

The value of capacitor C2 is multipled by the gain of Q1 and a much larger capacitor is "electrically" connected at TP5. If the

284

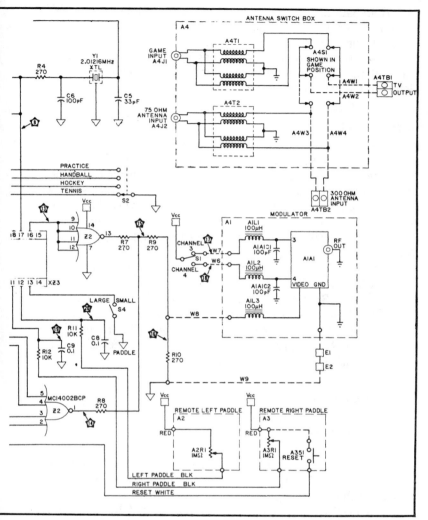

capacitor were opened or completely left out of the base circuit, little effect would be noticed with game operation when using batteries. However, with AC operation, hum bars might be seen on the TV screen. Hum bars usually show up as dark bands that drift up or down the screen. These bars are caused by ripple voltage from the rectified AC which will distort the video waveform. The action of C2 and Q1 help eliminate ripple to less than 0.01 volt. Note that hum bars can also be caused by the power supply in the TV set used for the game display.

Hum bars may be tolerable on the screen when viewing TV programs, but with video games that have straight vertical and horizontal lines, hum bars can become objectional. Usually, ripple will cause distortion of the vertical lines by putting a small bend in them. It will be your analysis to determine if the hum bars are a defect in the game console or in the TV set monitor.

Crystal Oscillator

A square wave of 2.01216 MHz should be found at TP8. The CMOS gate used as the active portion of the oscillator is operating as a linear device and not as a digital device. Consequently, the square wave will have sloping rise and fall times, and slightly rounded logic levels. Note the oscillator circuit shown in Fig. 11-3. Instruments used to measure the frequency or analyze the waveform should have a high impedance and less than 50-pF capacitance.

Problems that could prevent the oscillator from working could be a shorted capacitor, open PC runs, a defective IC, or a bad crystal. Pins 2, 3 and 4 of Z1 must be tied to ground for the circuit to operate. R5 must be present since this resistor sets up the bias for Z1. R4 could be shorted and the oscillator would still work, but if R4 were to open, the oscillator would not work. Also check L3 for an open since it supplies power.

MOS Game Circuit

You should handle (CMOS chip) with care. If possible, handle it by the case and do not touch the leads. A static charge could damage the IC.

Because all game functions and video signal are generated by Z3, the major problems with the game will usually be associated with Z3 or the controlling circuitry. Check for power V_{cc} voltage, V_c voltage and power ground points of Z3. If they are OK, check TP9 for a high (almost V_c). If TP9 is low (almost ground), Z3 is held in reset all the time and it will appear not to function. The circuitry associated with TP9 is part of Z1, R6 and reset switch A3S1. If TP9 appears low all the time, measure the voltage at TP10 (use a high-impedance voltmeter or scope). If this point is low, then either Z1 is bad, or there is an open or short along the PC runs of Z1. If TP10 is high, then check A3S1. It could be operating such that it is closed all the time or its contacts could be bent and therefore shorting.

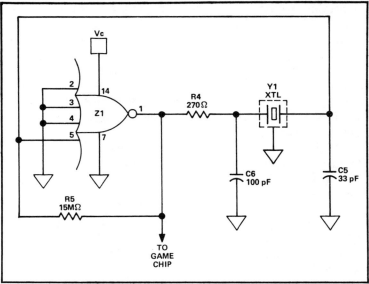

Fig. 11-3. Crystal oscillator circuit.

Audio Amplifier

The audio output from Z3 is at pin 3 or TP11. The tone burst
goes from a ground level to V_c level. If you see tone action at TP11
and the speaker is not beeping, check for proper operation of Q2. If
Q2 is OK, check for poor solder joints around R2. If R2 is also OK,
check the speaker for continuity and check the associated PC board
runs. Notice that the audio network receives its power from the
unregulated side of Q1.

Video Processing

The video processor NOR gate Z2 inverts, mixes and buffers
all video and sync signals for the modulator. The sync signals at
TP13 are easily seen with an oscilloscope, but the video at TP14 is
difficult to see unless you have a scope with high vertical amplifier
gain. The best test for this section is the TV set itself. Since left and
right players (paddle) video, ball video and the score and field video
are all outputted on separate pins of Z3, it is a simple matter to
determine what pin you would suspect is opened or shorted if the
ball or paddle is missing from the screen.

An open input to Z2 would probably be harder to isolate than a
shorted (to ground) pin. For example, let's say pin 5 of Z2 (left
player video input) is shorted to ground. The TV screen will show a

normal video pattern, except the left player paddle will be missing. If pin 5 of Z2 is open (or shorted to V_{cc}), the TV screen will appear to be synced up properly but there will be no video at all. An open or short to V_{cc} on pin 2, 3, or 4 of Z2 would cause this same blank field.

Notice that the sync half of Z2 has all its inputs tied together. All we need here is an inverter and not a mixer. Pin 16 of Z3 is normally high. During vertical and horizontal time, pin 16 of Z3 goes low. This means that pin 13 of Z2 goes high during sync time, but is held low during video time.

Mixing the video and the sync pulses together is handled by R7, R8, R9 and R10. If you look at TP15 with an oscilloscope, you will find a composite video signal of about 4 volts peak-to-peak. The video levels are from 0 volts to about 2 volts. The sync levels are from 2 volts to about 4 volts. R9 and R10 form a single voltage divider network that chops this 4 volts down to less than 2 volts, which is the maximum that should be applied to the modulator. Problems with these resistors will usually be limited to poor solder joints or PC board run problems.

Modulator

Due to FCC requirements, the modulator unit should not be repaired. If you find proper voltages, grounds and video levels entering the modulator and there is no picture on the TV screen, replace the modulator.

Antenna Switch Box

Except for opens or shorts, about the only problem you should find in the switch box is loose components. Make sure all devices have good solder connections and that all hardware is tight and making good ground connections. Insure that the internal shielding within the box is not shorting any wires. Also, make sure that the rivets holding the shielding, the terminal strip and isolation switch are tight. The best test for the switch box is actually connecting it to a TV monitor and feeding video into it. Check for picture sharpness and any show that would indicate a weak signal.

Remote Paddle Controls

Problems with the remote paddle controls should be limited to wiring problems within the cables and problems with switches and controls. Electrical problems may show up as disappearing paddles, or there may be a "no man's" area on the screen where the paddles

Table 11-1. Troubleshooting Chart.

INDICATION	PROBABLE FAULT	LOOK FOR
Audio OK but no picture	Antenna Switch Box	Broken coax-A4S1 not in Game position. Box not properly connected to TV.
	Modulator	Open A1L1 or A1L2-Open A1L3.
	Video Mixer	Bad Z2 or an open or shorted PC connector.
Picture faded, no contrast control, audio OK	Video Mixer	Z2 not MC14002BCP (MC14002CP is not to be used for Z2).
Paddles jerk more than 1" every time speaker beeps	Power Supply	Weak batteries-AC line too low (AC Adapter)-Short in audio section-Intermittent L1 or L2-Shorted CR2 Defective Q1.
Audio weak, good picture	Audio Section	R2 not of proper value-Q2 defective-Speaker defective-
Dead game, no audio or video	Power Supply	Open Q1-Shorted C2 Shorted CR1 Open S6 or L1-Broken J1.
	Oscillator	Shorted PC runs-Shorted C6 or C5 Open input to Z3-Bad Z1 or Y1-Bad solder joints-Jumper broken or missing.
	Reset Circuit	A3S1 shorted-Z1 or Z3 bad.
Picture OK but no audio	Audio Section	Open or shorted Q2-Opened LS1-Bad solder joints or PC runs.
Picture OK, but hum bars present i when AC adapter is used.	Power Supply	Open C2-Bad Q1 or CR1.
No ball, score or field.	Video Section (video)	Z2 is bad or the input is shorted-Z3 not reset. Press the reset button.
Picture is OK, but no paddles	Video Section (video)	Z2 bad or shorted-Z3 not reset. Press the reset button-A2R1 or A3R1 bad or wrong position-C8 or C9 opened-Bad solder joint on R12, R11.

Table 11-1. Troubleshooting Chart (continued from page 289.

INDICATION	PROBABLE FAULT	LOOK FOR
Picture shows hockey and 5 paddles all the time in one or all game positions	Game Select Switch	S2 bad or bad ground- PC run short.
No speed, slice or paddle options	Chip Control	Bad switch (S3, S4, S5)- PC run short or open.
No picture on Channel 3, OK on Channel 4	Modulator Control	S1 bad- Modulator bad- Modulator coil open.
Picture on Channel 3 and Channel 4	Modulator Control	S1 bad or solder short- Modulator power input shorted.
Picture OK, but weak diagonal lines present	Antenna Switch Box	Broken balun coil- Bad switch- Open ground.
Audio on for too long a time after ball rebound	Audio Section	Missing jumper wire (Pin 3 to 27) on Z3
Paddle jitters at random rate	Power Supply	C7 opened or missing.

are hard to control or position in this area. Also, make sure that the paddle controls will move the paddles all the way off the screen in both directions. If capacitors C9 and C8 are open, then the waveform at TP 19 will be a negative-going pulse with no ramping of the waveform.

Refer to Table 11-1 for more troubleshooting information. Also, the schematics for the Radio Shack model 60-3052 video game is shown in Fig. 11-4.

RCA STUDIO II VIDEO GAME

Th RCA Studio II home video game programmer uses the COSMAC microprocessor, along with a plug-in memory, to provide a versatile game and educational format. The complete Studio II system is shown in Fig. 11-5.

Studio II uses RCA's single-chip version of the COSMAC microprocessor, the CDP1802, which provides central computer control for the various game, educational, and other entertainment programs. Thus, a very high level of program sophistication can be achieved, limited only by the solid-state memory capacity. The system remains flexible and can be updated through the expedient use of plug-in program cards. The Studio II's logic is based on the modified FRED system. The complete unit connects to the VHF

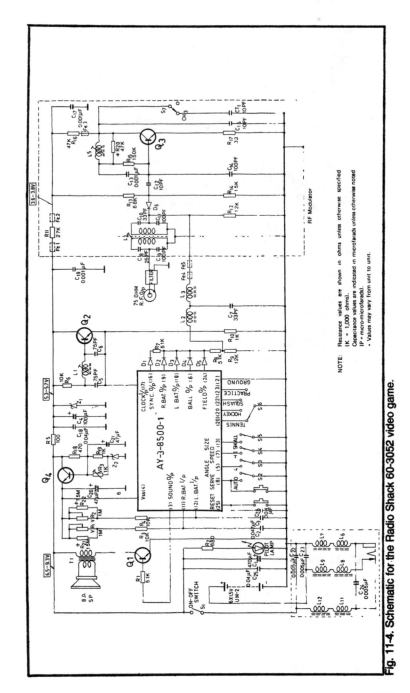

Fig. 11-4. Schematic for the Radio Shack 60-3052 video game.

NOTE: Resistance values are shown in ohms unless otherwise specified
1K = 1,000 ohms).
Capacitance values are indicated in microfarads unless otherwise noted
(P = micro-microfarad).
• Values may vary from unit to unit.

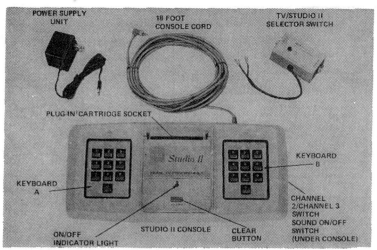

Fig. 11-5. The RCA Studio II game system.

antenna terminals of a standard television receiver. Two, 10-digit keyboards located on the main housing let the players control the display and select the game to be played.

The system has three major units as follows. The main-control console contains the keyboards and electronics for selecting and processing the programs. The selector switch box controls power to the control console and connects either the TV antenna or the rf output cable from the game to the receiver antenna terminals. The power supply plugs into the wall AC outlet and supplies 9 VDC to the control console via the selector switch box and rf output cable. Supplementing the programs built into the fixed ROM of the control console, some plug-in cartridges have been programmed with additional entertainment formats.

System Operation

The game system can be divided into eight sections:

■ Microprocessor.
■ Memory system consisting of read-only memories (ROMs) and random-access memories (RAMs).
■ Player/keyboard interface.
■ Video display generator.
■ Sound circuit.
■ rf oscillator/modulator section.
■ Selector switch box.
■ DC power supply.

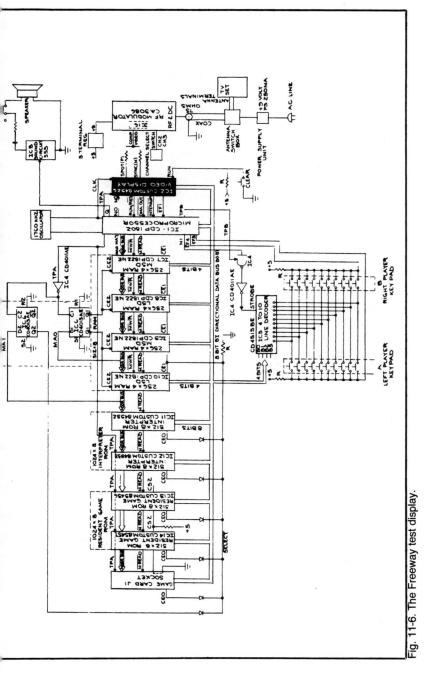

Fig. 11-6. The Freeway test display.

293

The heart of Studio II is RCA's type CDP1802 COSMAC microprocessor. The CDP1802 is an LSI CMOS, 8-bit, register-oriented CPU. For this application, it is operated at 5 VDC and at a clock frequency of 1.760 MHz.

When the CLEAR button is pressed, the microprocessor registers are reset. A game is selected from the ROMs by entering the proper code via the key pad buttons. The game starts as the microprocessor executes the program instructions contained in the ROMs.

The Memory

The memory has 2048 bytes of ROM and 512 bytes of RAM. For programs contained in the resident or external ROM memory devices, 1024 bytes of ROM are used as an interpreter language. The interpreter ROM provides common game display patterns, score keeping, subroutines, etc. The remaining 1024 bytes of ROM are mask-programmed resident game formats. The RAMs are used for TV refresh, stack and variable storage. Data bytes can be written into the RAM (memory write, MWR) or readout of the RAM (memory read, MRD) on command of the microprocessor. When a program cartridge is plugged into the control socket, the resident memory (ROM) is deselected and operation proceeds by using the cartridge memory (ROM).

The Keyboards

Two 10-key pads provide the player/keyboard interface. The key pads were specifically developed for the RCA Studio II video game. The keys are arranged in the standard telephone-type format. Keyboards were selected in lieu of other ways of player interface because they provided the flexibility of permitting specific numerical entries as well as motion and direction entries.

System Test Procedures

Press the CLEAR button on the console and then press key 4 on the left-hand keyboard. This sets up the game for Freeway, and the track as shown in Fig. 11-6 should appear immediately. If necessary, adjust the fine tuning and hold controls of the TV for best picture.

Operational Checks With The Test Cartridge

The test cartridge, which plugs into the cartridge slot on the Studio II console, scans the digital circuitry for trouble with a

294

routine that takes about 30 seconds. If it finds a malfunction, this will be indicated on the TV screen. If there is no trouble, the cartridge sets up a test for the two keyboards. Note that when using the test cartridge, use a 500-mA power supply.

Press and hold the CLEAR button on the Studio II console. Insert the Tester 1 cartridge into the slot while holding the CLEAR button. Now release the CLEAR button. A pattern similar to that in the top of Fig. 11-7 should appear on the screen immediately, and Tester 1 begins its scan of the system (indicated by the black streak moving through the white field in the lower half of the pattern). If the pattern fails to appear or a pattern other than that shown appears, a defective chip is indicated.

In about 11 seconds, the first scan is complete. The display shifts to the second pattern shown in Fig. 11-7 with a white streak scanning a black field. This scan takes another 11 seconds. At the end of the second scan, the system changes the pattern on the lower half to a series of transient vertical white lines on black and then a series of black lines on white. This sequence takes about two seconds. At the end of this short sequence, the pattern shifts to the third pattern shown in Fig. 11-7. This indicates that all memories are operational. A digit or digits appearing in the checkerboard pattern in the center of the screen, as shown in the bottom pattern of Fig. 11-7 indicates chip failure in the PC board.

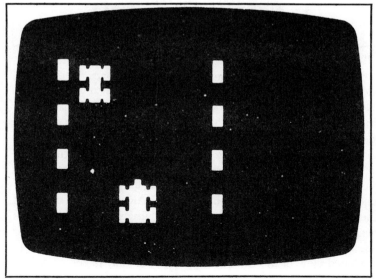

Fig. 11-7. Various Tester 1 screen patterns.

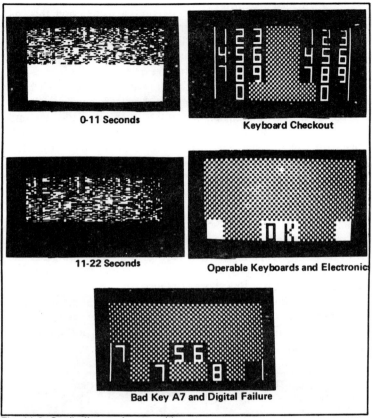

0-11 Seconds

Keyboard Checkout

11-22 Seconds

Operable Keyboards and Electronic

Bad Key A7 and Digital Failure

Fig. 11-8. Studio II console assembly.

If the checkerboard appears as in the third pattern, touch the keys—one at a time—of the keyboard A, and then keyboard B. As each key switch closes, the digit on the screen should change to a checkerboard square. If any digit remains on the screen after the key is pressed, the keyboard is defective and must be replaced. When all key closures are complete (indicating satisfactory keyboard function), the video screen shifts to the OK pattern as shown in the fourth pattern. The pattern flip flops between black-on-white and white-on-black until the CLEAR button is actuated. If the CLEAR button functions normally, the whole sequence starts again as the button is released. This is the complete Studio II Tester 1 test program that is performed with the test cartridge. A complete exploded view of the Studio II console assembly is shown in Fig. 11-8.

MOTOROLA VIDEO MODULATOR MC1372 CHIP

The Motorola MC1372 chip can be used with video games to generate rf TV signals from color-difference and luminance signals. Referring to the block diagram in Fig. 11-9 we see the MC1372 contains a chroma subcarrier oscillator, lead and lag networks, chroma modulator, an RF oscillator and modulator amd a TTL compatible clock driver with adjustable duty cycle. This color TV video modulator IC is also used in test instruments and video tape recorders.

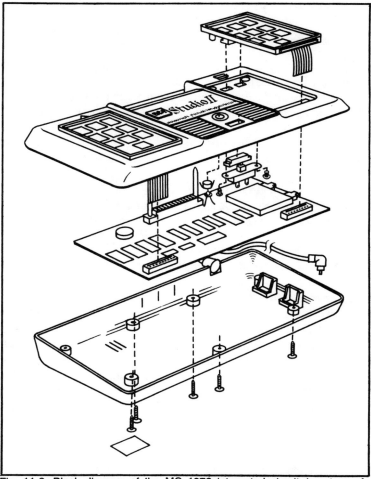

Fig. 11-9. Block diagram of the MC 1372 integrated circuit (courtesy of Motorola).

Operational Description and Chip Pinout

Refer to the circuit of the MC1372 chip in Figs. 11-10 and 11-11.

Pin 1-Clock Output. This provides a rectangular pulse output waveform with a frequency equal to the chrominance subcarrier oscillator. The output is capable of driving one LS-TTL load.

Pin 2-Oscillator Input. This is the color subcarrier oscillator feedback input. The signal from the clock output is externally phase-shifted and AC-coupled to this pin.

Pin 3-Duty Cycle Adjust. A DC voltage applied to this pin adjusts the duty cycle of the clock output signal. If the pin is left unconnected, the duty cycle is approximately 50 percent.

Pin 4-Ground.

Pin 5-Color B Input. This is a DC-coupled input to chroma modulator B, whose phase leads modulator A by approximately 100 degrees. The modulator output amplitude and polarity correspond to the voltage difference between this pin and the color reference voltage at pin 6.

Pin 6-Color Reference Input. The DC voltage applied to this pin establishes the reference voltage to which color A and color B inputs are compared.

Pin 7-Color A Output. This is a DC-coupled input to chroma modulator A, whose phase lags modulator B by approximately 100 degrees. The modulator output amplitude and polarity correspond to the voltage difference between this pin and the color reference voltage at pin 6.

Pin 8-Chroma Modulator Output. This is a low-impedance (emitter-follower) output which provides the vectorial sum of chroma modulators A and B.

Pin 9-Luminance Input. This is the input to the RF modulator. This pin accepts a DC-coupled luminance and sync signal. The amplitude of the rf signal output increases with positive voltage applied to the pin, and ground potential results in zero output. A signal with positive-going sync should be used.

Pin 10-Chrominance Input. This pin supplies input to the rf modulator and accepts AC-coupled chrominance provided by the chroma modulator output (pin 8). The signal is reduced by an internal resistor divider before being applied to the rf modulator. The resistor divider consists of a 300-ohm series resistor and a 500-ohm shunt resistor. Additional gain reduction may be obtained by the addition of external series resistance to pin 10.

Pin 11-V$_{cc}$. Positive power supply.

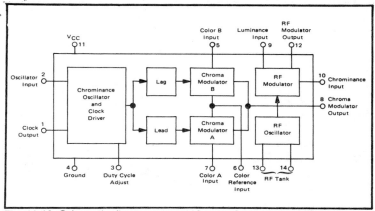

Fig. 11-10. Schematic diagram of the MC1372 IC (courtesy of Motorola).

Pin 12-RF Modulator Output. This is the common collector of the output modulator stage. Output impedance and stage gain may be selected by choice of register connected between this pin and the DC supply.

Pins 13 and 14-RF Tank. A tuned circuit is connected between these pins to determine the rf oscillator frequency. The tuned circuit must provide a low DC resistance shunt. Applying a DC offset voltage between these pins results in base-band composite video at the rf modulator output.

MC1372 Circuit Description

The chrominance oscillator and clock driver consists of emitter-follower Q4 and inverting amplifier Q5. The signal presented at clock driver output pin 1 is coupled to oscillator input pin 2 through an external RC and crystal network, which provides 180-degree phase shift at the resonant frequency. The duty cycle of the output waveform is determined by the DC component at pin 1 internally coupled through R12 to the base of Q4. As pin 1 DC voltage increases, a smaller portion of the sinusiodal feedback signal at pin 2 exceeds the Q4 base voltage of two times VBE required for conduction. As the DC level is reduced, device Q4—and thus Q5—is turned on for a longer time of the cycle. Transistors Q0, Q1, Q2 and diode D1 provide the biasing network that determines the DC operating level of the oscillator. The transistors Q2 and resistors R5, R6 and R7 form a voltage reference of four times VBE at collector of Q2. The DC voltage at pin 1 is determined by the value of R4, R8 and R12, and the applied duty cycle adjusts the voltage at

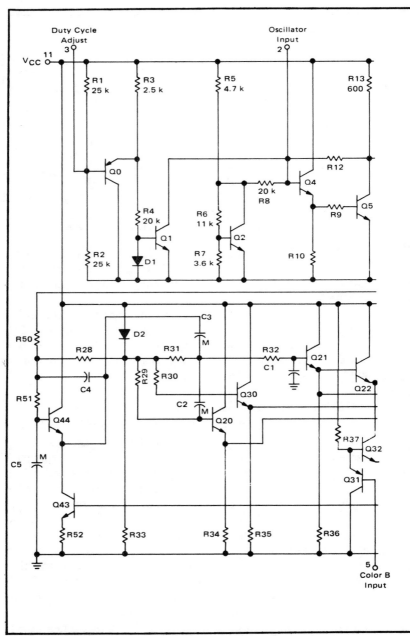

Fig. 11-11. Typical application circuit block diagram for the MC1372 video modulator chip (courtesy of Motorola).

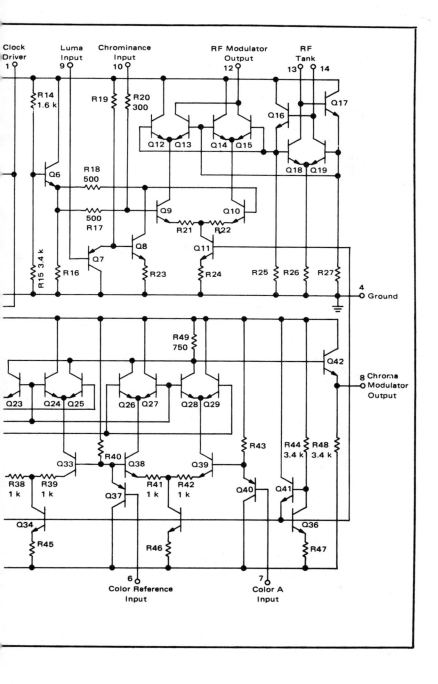

301

pin 3. Since these resistors are nominally equal, the voltage at pin 1 will always approximate the DC voltage at pin 3.

The oscillator signal at pin 1 is internally coupled to active filter Q44. This filter reduces the frequency content above 4 MHz. The output of the filter at the emitter of Q44 is AC-coupled through C3 to the input of lead/lag network. R32 and C1 provide about 50 degrees of phase lag, while C2 and R29 provide about 50 degrees of phase lead. These two quasi-quadrature waveforms are used to switch chroma modulators B and A, respectively. The transistors Q22 through Q25 and Q32-33 form a doubly balanced modulator. The input signal fed to pin 5 is compared to the color DC reference voltage applied at pin 6 of the differential amplifiers. The source current provided by Q34 is partioned in Q32 and Q33 according to the differential input signal. The bases of transistors Q23 and Q24 are connected to the DC reference voltage at the emitter of Q30. The base of transistors Q22 and Q25 are connected to the phase-delayed oscillator signal at the emitter of buffer transistor Q21. The differential signal currents provided by Q32 and Q33 are switched to transistors Q22 through Q25, and the resultant signal voltage is developed across R49. This signal has the phase and frequency of the oscillator signal at the emitter of Q21. The amplitude is proportional to the differential input signal applied between 5 and 6. Transistors Q26 through Q29 and Q38 and Q39 form chroma demodulator B. This modulator develops a signal voltage that is proportional to the differential voltage applied between pins 6 and 7. The phase and frequency of the output is equal to the phase-advanced chroma oscillator at the emitter of the buffer transistor Q20. Both chroma modulators A and B share the same output resistor, R49, so the output signal presented at the emitter of Q42 (pin 8) is the algebraic sum of modulators A and B.

The rf oscillator consists of differential amplifier Q18 and Q19 cross-coupled through emitter followers Q16 and Q17. The oscillator will operate at the parallel resonant frequency of the network connected between pins 13 and 14. The oscillator output is used to switch the doubly balanced rf modulator, Q9 through Q15. Transistors Q7 and Q9 provide level shifting and a high input impedance to the luminance input at pin 9. The bases of transistors Q9 and Q10 are both biased through resistors R17 and R18, respectively, to the same DC reference source voltage at Q6 emitter. The base voltage of Q10 may only be offset in a negative direction by luminance signal current source Q8. This design insures that overmodulation due to the luminance signal will never occur.

The chrominance signal developed at pin 8 is externally AC-coupled to pin 10 where it is reduced by resistor dividers R20 and R17 and added to the luminance signal in Q9. The resultant differential composite video currents are switched at the appropriate rf frequency in Q12 through Q15. The output signal current is presented at pin 12. Transistors Q36 and Q41 and resistors R44 and R47 provide a highly stable voltage reference for biasing current sources for transistors Q43, Q34, Q35 and Q11.

Index